PRENTICE HALL LITERATURE

SIGHTLINES 8

Alice Barlow-Kedves

Thora O'Grady

Judy Onody

Wendy Mathieu

Susan Tywoniuk

PRENTICE HALL GINN CANADA

SightLines 8
Canadian Cataloguing in Publication Data
Main entry under title:
SightLines 8 anthology
(Prentice Hall literature)
ISBN 0-13-012905-4
I. Readers (Elementary). I. Barlow-Kedves, Alice
II. Series: Sightlines (Scarborough, ON)
PE1121.S524 1999 428'6 C99-930139-x

Prentice-Hall, Inc., Upper Saddle River, New Jersey
Prentice-Hall International, Inc., London
Prentice-Hall of Australia, Pty., Ltd., Sydney
Prentice Hall of India Pvt., Ltd., New Delhi
Prentice-Hall of Japan, Inc., Tokyo
Prentice-Hall of Southeast Asia (PTE) Ltd., Singapore
Editora Prentice-Hall do Brasil Ltda., Rio de Janeiro
Prentice-Hall Hispanoamericana, S.A., Mexico

ISBN 0-13-012905-4

Publisher: Carol Stokes
Project Manager: Helen Mason
Project Editor and Anthologist: Irene Cox
Production Editor: Karen Alliston
Director of Secondary Publishing: MaryLynne Meschino
Copy Editor: Denyse O'Leary
Production Co-ordinator: Sharon Houston
Permissions: Jeanne Duperreault
Interior Design: Zena Denchik
Cover Design: Alex Li
Cover Image: Harvey Chan
Page Layout: Jack Steiner

Printed and bound in Canada
6   03

Prentice Hall Canada wishes to acknowledge the following text and visuals researchers:

Leslie Kestin
Tessa McWatt
Catherine Rondina
Elma Schemenauer
Jennifer Sweeney
Heli Kivilaht
Keltie Thomas
Laurie Seidlitz
Martha DiLeonardo
Monika Croydon
Nancy Mackenzie
Rita Vanden Heuvel
Tracey Shreve-Williams

Prentice Hall Canada wishes to thank the following:

Assessment Consultant: Michael Stubitsch
Equity Reviewer: Elizabeth Parchment
Aboriginal Content Consultant: Rocky Landon
Grade 8 Reviewers:
Joan Penny Lorintt, BC
Stuart Bent, BC
Melody Sawkins, BC
Lily Pentek, AB
Toni d'Apice, AB
Al Dixon, AB
Leigh Morris, ON
Susan Dunlop, ON
Nancy Palarchio, ON
Linda Laliberte, AB
David Graham, BC

Contents by Unit

Look

Look Closely

Look Back

Look Beyond

Contents by Genre

Nonfiction

Poetry

Short Stories

Oral Pieces

Visuals

Welcome to *SightLines*

The *SightLines* student anthologies offer a wide range of high-quality, high-interest literature by both new and established Canadian and world writers. Each *SightLines* anthology features the following:

- A wide range of texts:
  - fiction, including short stories, poems, drama
  - nonfiction, including essays, newspaper, and magazine articles
  - stand-alone visuals such as paintings, photographs, and technical art
  - transactional texts such as instructional material, web-site pages, graphs and charts

- A wide range of reading levels

- Texts geared to a wide variety of learning styles

- Learning outcomes boxes called "Focus Your Learning" and activities for each selection

- Tables of contents by theme and genre

- Author/artist biographies

look

1

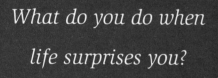

What do you do when

life surprises you?

❚ ❚ ❚

Sometimes what you expect
is very different from "the
real story." Get ready for a
series of double-takes! See if
you can stay one step ahead
as you look…then look again.

The Street That Got Mislaid

PATRICK
WADDINGTON

Marc Girondin had worked in the filing section of the City Hall's engineering department for so long that the city was laid out in his mind like a map, full of names and places, intersecting streets and streets that led nowhere, blind alleys and winding lanes.

In all Montreal no one possessed such knowledge; a dozen policemen and taxi drivers together could not rival him. That is not to say that he actually knew the streets whose names he could recite like a series of incantations, for he did little walking. He knew simply of their existence, where they were, and in what relation they stood to others.

But it was enough to make him a specialist. He was undisputed expert of the filing cabinets where all the particulars of all the streets from Abbott to Zotique were indexed, back, forward, and across. Those aristocrats, the engineers, the inspectors of water mains, and the like, all came to him when they wanted some little particular, some detail, in a hurry. They might despise him as a lowly clerk, but they needed him all the same.

Marc much preferred his office, despite the profound lack of excitement of his work, to his room on Oven Street (running north and south from Sherbrooke East to St. Catherine), where his neighbours were noisy and sometimes violent and his landlady consistently so. He tried to explain the meaning of his existence once to a fellow tenant, Louis, but without much success. Louis, when he got the drift, was apt to sneer.

"So Craig latches on to Bleury and Bleury gets to be Park, so who cares? Why the excitement?"

"I will show you," said Marc. "Tell me, first, where you live."

"Are you crazy? Here on Oven Street. Where else?"

"How do you know?"

"How do I know? I'm here, ain't I? I pay my rent, don't I? I get my mail here, don't I?"

Marc shook his head patiently.

"None of that is evidence," he said. "You live here on Oven Street because it says so in my filing cabinet at City Hall. The Post Office sends you mail because my card index tells it to. If my cards didn't say so, you wouldn't exist and Oven Street wouldn't either. That, my friend, is the triumph of bureaucracy."

Louis walked away in disgust. "Try telling that to the landlady," he muttered.

So Marc continued on his undistinguished career, his fortieth birthday came and went without remark, day after day passed uneventfully. A street was renamed, another constructed, a third widened; it all went carefully into the files, back, forward, and across.

And then something happened that filled him with amazement, shocked him beyond measure, and made the world of the filing cabinets tremble to their steel bases.

One August afternoon, opening a drawer to its fullest extent, he felt something catch. Exploring farther, he discovered a card stuck at the back between the top and bottom. He drew it out and found it to be an old index card, dirty and torn, but still perfectly decipherable. It was labelled "Rue de la Bouteille Verte" or "Green Bottle Street."

Marc stared at it in wonder. He had never heard of the place or of anything resembling so odd a name. Undoubtedly it had been retitled in some other fashion befitting the modern tendency. He checked the listed details and ruffled confidently through the master file of street names. It was not there. He made another search, careful and protracted, through the cabinets. There was nothing. Absolutely nothing.

Once more he examined the card. There was no mistake. The date of the last regular street inspection was exactly fifteen years, five months, and fourteen days ago.

As the awful truth burst upon him, Marc dropped the card in

horror, then pounced on it again fearfully, glancing over his shoulder as he did so.

It was lost, a forgotten street. For fifteen years and more it had existed in the heart of Montreal, less than a kilometre from City Hall, and no one had known. It had simply dropped out of sight, a stone in water.

In his heart Marc had sometimes dreamed of such a possibility. There were so many obscure places, twisting lanes, and streets jumbled together as intricately as an Egyptian labyrinth. But of course it could not happen, not with the omniscient file at hand. Only it had. And it was dynamite. It would blow the office sky-high.

Vaguely, in his consternation, Marc remembered how, some time after he first started to work, his section had been moved to another floor. The old-fashioned files were discarded and all the cards made out afresh. It must have been at that time that Green Bottle Street was stuck between the upper and lower drawers.

He put the card in his pocket and went home to reflect. That night he slept badly and monstrous figures flitted through his dreams. Among them appeared a gigantic likeness of his chief going mad and forcing him into a red-hot filing cabinet.

The next day he made up his mind. Pleading illness, he took the afternoon off and with beating heart went looking for the street.

Although he knew the location perfectly, he passed it twice and had to retrace his steps. Baffled, he closed his eyes, consulted his mind's infallible map, and walked directly to the entry. It was so narrow that he could touch the adjoining walls with his outstretched hands. A metre or so from the sidewalk was a tall and solid wooden structure, much weatherbeaten, with a simple latched door in the centre. This he opened and stepped inside. Green Bottle Street lay before him.

It was perfectly real, and reassuring as well. On either side of a cobbled pavement were three small houses, six in all, each with a diminutive garden in front, spaced off by low iron palings of a kind that has disappeared except in the oldest quarters. The houses looked extremely neat and well-kept and the cobbles appeared to have been recently watered and swept. Windowless brick walls of ancient warehouses encircled the six homes and joined at the farther end of the street.

At his first glance, Marc realized how it had got its unusual name. It was exactly like a bottle in shape.

With the sun shining on the stones and garden plots, and the blue sky overhead, the street gave him a momentary sense of well-being and peace. It was completely charming, a scene from a print of fifty years ago.

A woman who Marc guessed was some sixty years of age was watering roses in the garden of the first house to his right. She gazed at him motionless, and the water flowed from her can unheeded to the ground. He took off his hat and announced:

"I'm from the city engineering department, madame."

The woman recovered herself and set her watering can down.

"So you have found out at last," she said.

At these words, Marc's reborn belief that after all he had made a harmless and ridiculous error fled precipitately. There was no mistake.

"Tell me, please," he said tonelessly.

It was a curious story. For several years, she said, the tenants of Green Bottle Street had lived in amity with each other and the landlord, who also resided in one of the little houses. The owner became so attached to them that in a gesture of goodwill he deeded them his property, together with a small sum of money, when he died.

"We paid our taxes," the woman said, "and made out a multitude of forms and answered the questions of various officials at regular intervals, about our property. Then after a while we were sent no notices, so we paid no more taxes. No one bothered us at all. It was a

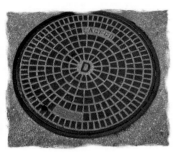

long time before we understood that in some way they'd forgotten about us."

Marc nodded. Of course, if Green Bottle Street had dropped from the ken of City Hall, no inspectors would go there, no census takers, no tax collectors. All would pass merrily by, directed elsewhere by the infallible filing cabinet.

"Then Michael Flanagan, who lives at number four," she went on, "a most interesting man, you must meet him—Mr. Flanagan called us together and said that if miracles happened, we should aid and abet them. It was he who had the door built and put up at the entrance to keep out passers-by or officials who might come along. We used to keep it locked, but it's been so long since anyone came that we don't bother now."

"Oh, there were many little things we had to do, like getting our mail at the Post Office and never having anything delivered at the door. Now almost the only visits we make to the outside world are to buy our food and clothes."

"And there has never been any change here all that time?" Marc asked.

"Yes, two of our friends died and their rooms were empty for a while. Then Jean Desselin, he's in number six, and sometimes goes into the city, returned with a Mr. Plonsky, a refugee. Mr. Plonsky was very tired and worn-out with his travellings and gladly moved in with us. Miss Hunter in number three brought home a very nice person, a distant relative, I believe. They quite understand the situation."

"And you, madame?" Marc inquired.

"My name is Sara Trusdale, and I have lived here for more than twenty years. I hope to end my days here as well."

She smiled pleasantly at him, apparently forgetting for the moment that he carried in his pocket a grenade that could blow their little world to pieces.

All of them, it seemed, had had their troubles, their losses, and failures before they found themselves in this place of refuge, this Green Bottle Street. To Marc, conscious of his own unsatisfactory existence, it sounded entrancing. He fingered the card in his pocket uncertainly.

"Mr. Plonsky and Mr. Flanagan took a great liking to each other," Miss Trusdale continued. "Both of them have been travellers and they like to talk about the things they have seen. Miss Hunter plays the piano and gives us concerts. Then there's Mr. Hazard and Mr. Desselin, who are very fond of chess and who brew wine in the cellar. For myself, I have my flowers and my books. It has been very enjoyable for all of us."

Marc and Miss Trusdale sat on her front step for a long time in silence. The sky's blue darkened, the sun disappeared behind the warehouse wall on the left.

"You remind me of my nephew," Miss Trusdale said suddenly. "He was a dear boy. I was heartbroken when he died in the influenza epidemic after the war. I'm the last of my family, you know."

Marc could not recall when he had been spoken to with such simple, if indirect, goodwill. His heart warmed to this old lady. Obscurely he felt on the verge of a great moral discovery. He took the card out of his pocket.

"I found this yesterday in the filing cabinet," he said. "No one else knows about it yet. If it should come out, there would be a great scandal and no end of trouble for all of you as well. Newspaper reporters, tax collectors ..."

He thought again of his landlady, his belligerent neighbours, his room that defied improvement.

"I wonder now," he said slowly, "I am a good tenant, and I wonder ..."

"Oh yes," she leaned forward eagerly, "you could have the top floor of my house. I have more space than I know what to do with. I'm sure it would suit you. You must come and see it right away."

The mind of Marc Girondin, filing clerk, was made up. With a gesture of renunciation he tore the card across and dropped the pieces in the watering can. As far as he was concerned, Green Bottle Street would remain mislaid forever.

Activities

1. What techniques does the author use to portray Green Bottle Street as a kind of forgotten paradise?

2. Imagine you are a news reporter who has heard of this story. Write a live television news report about it, and perform the broadcast for the class.

3. Imagine that the residents of Green Bottle Street have been invited to a radio or television talk show to be interviewed about their experiences. In a small group, role-play the show. Include a host, experts, and audience members, as well as the residents of the street.

Optrick Larry Evans

This maze, which has the illusion of three dimensions, was created using a computer. With your finger, trace your way from the start arrow in the lower-left corner to the end point at the upper right.

Activities

1. Count how many levels, or planes, are represented in this picture. Then, in a small group, come to an agreement on the number of levels, and present your findings to the class. Next, analyse how the computer artist made this flat image look three-dimensional. Explain your ideas to the group.

2. Collect a variety of other optical illusions. Make a bulletin board display of the illusions you have found. Compare and contrast them. As a class, discuss why they work.

Thank You, Ma'am

LANGSTON
HUGHES

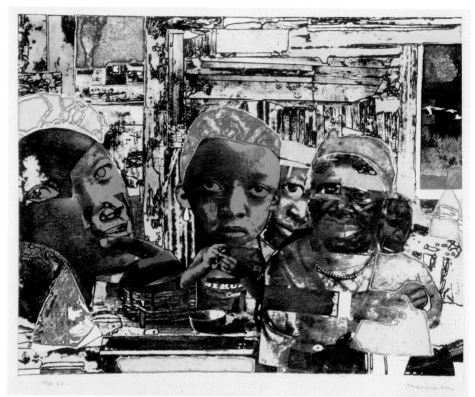

The Train Romare Bearden, ©Romare Bearden 1999/VIS*ART Copyright Inc.

She was a large woman with a large purse that had everything in it but a hammer and nails.

It had a long strap, and she carried it slung across her shoulder. It was about eleven o'clock at night, dark, and she was walking alone, when a boy ran up behind her and tried to snatch her purse. The strap broke with the sudden single tug the boy gave it from behind. But the boy's weight and the weight of the purse combined caused him to lose his balance. Instead of taking off full blast as he had hoped, the boy fell on his back on the sidewalk and his legs flew up. The large woman simply turned around and kicked him right square in his blue-jeaned sitter. Then she reached down, picked the boy up by his shirt front, and shook him until his teeth rattled.

After that the woman said, "Pick up my pocketbook, boy, and give it here."

She still held him tightly. But she bent down enough to permit him to stoop and pick up her purse. Then she said, "Now ain't you ashamed of yourself?"

Firmly gripped by his shirt front, the boy said, "Yes'm."

The woman said, "What did you want to do it for?"

The boy said, "I didn't aim to."

She said, "You a lie!"

By that time two or three people passed, stopped, turned to look, and some stood watching.

"If I turn you loose, will you run?" asked the woman.

"Yes'm," said the boy.

"Then I won't turn you loose," said the woman. She did not release him.

"Lady, I'm sorry," whispered the boy.

"Um-hum! Your face is dirty. I got a great mind to wash your face for you. Ain't you got nobody home to tell you to wash your face?"

"No'm," said the boy.

"Then it will get washed this evening," said the large woman, starting up the street, dragging the frightened boy behind her.

He looked as if he were fourteen or fifteen, frail and willow-wild, in tennis shoes and blue jeans.

The woman said, "You ought to be my son. I would teach you right from wrong. Least I can do right now is to wash your face. Are you hungry?"

"No'm," said the being-dragged boy. "I just want you to turn me loose."

"Was I bothering *you* when I turned that corner?" asked the woman.

"No'm."

"But you put yourself in contact with *me*," said the woman. "If you think that that contact is not going to last awhile, you got another thought coming. When I get through with you, sir, you are going to remember Mrs. Luella Bates Washington Jones."

Sweat popped out on the boy's face and he began to struggle. Mrs. Jones stopped, jerked him around in front of her, put a half nelson about his neck, and continued to drag him up the street. When she got to her door, she dragged the boy inside, down a hall, and into a large kitchenette-furnished room at the rear of the house. She switched on the light and left the door open. The boy could hear other roomers laughing and talking in the large house. Some of their doors were open, too, so he knew he and the woman were not alone. The woman still had him by the neck in the middle of her room.

She said, "What is your name?"

"Roger," answered the boy.

"Then, Roger, you go to that sink and wash your face," said the woman, whereupon she turned him loose—at last. Roger looked at the door, looked at the woman, looked at the door, *and went to the sink.*

"Let the water run until it gets warm," she said. "Here's a clean towel."

"You gonna take me to jail?" asked the boy, bending over the sink.

"Not with that face, I would not take you nowhere," said the woman. "Here I am trying to get home to cook me a bite to eat, and you snatch my pocketbook! Maybe you ain't been to your supper either, late as it be. Have you?"

"There's nobody home at my house," said the boy.

"Then we'll eat," said the woman. "I believe you're hungry, or been hungry, to try to snatch my pocketbook!"

"l want a pair of blue suede shoes," said the boy.

"Well, you didn't have to snatch *my* pocketbook to get some suede shoes," said Mrs. Luella Bates Washington Jones. "You could of asked me."

"Ma'am?"

The water dripping from his face, the boy looked at her. There was a long pause. A very long pause. After he had dried his face and not knowing what else to do, dried it again, the boy turned around, wondering what next. The door was open. He could make a dash for it down the hall. He could run, run, run, *run*!

The woman was sitting on the day bed. After a while she said, "I were young once and I wanted things I could not get."

There was another long pause. The boy's mouth opened. Then he frowned, not knowing he frowned.

The woman said, "Um-hum! You thought I was going to say *but*, didn't you? You thought I was going to say, *but I didn't snatch people's pocketbooks.* Well, I wasn't going to say that." Pause. Silence. "I have done things, too, which I would not tell you, son—neither tell God, if He didn't already know. Everybody's got something in common. So you set down while I fix us something to eat. You might run that comb through your hair so you will look presentable."

In another corner of the room behind a screen was a gas plate and an icebox. Mrs. Jones got up and went behind the screen. The woman did not watch the boy to see if he was going to run now, nor did she watch her purse, which she left behind her on the day bed. But the boy took care to sit on the far side of the room, away from the purse, where he thought she could easily see him out of the corner of her eye if she wanted to. He did not trust the woman *not* to trust him. And he did not want to be mistrusted now.

"Do you need somebody to go to the store," asked the boy, "maybe to get some milk or something?"

"Don't believe I do," said the woman, "unless you just want sweet milk yourself. I was going to make cocoa out of this canned milk I got here."

"That will be fine," said the boy.

She heated some lima beans and ham she had in the icebox, made the cocoa, and set the table. The woman did not ask the boy anything about where he lived, or his folks, or anything else that would embarrass him. Instead, as they ate, she told him about her job in a hotel beauty shop that stayed open late, what the work was like, and how all kinds of women came in and out, blondes, redheads, and Spanish. Then she cut him a half of her ten-cent cake.

"Eat some more, son," she said.

When they were finished eating, she got up and said, "Now here, take this ten dollars and buy yourself some blue suede shoes. And next time, do not make the mistake of latching onto *my* pocketbook *nor nobody else's*, because shoes got by devilish ways will burn your feet. I got to get my rest now. But from here on in, son, I hope you will behave yourself."

She led him down the hall to the front door and opened it. "Good night! Behave yourself, boy!" she said, looking out into the street as he went down the steps.

The boy wanted to say something other than, "Thank you, ma'am," to Mrs. Luella Bates Washington Jones, but although his lips moved, he couldn't even say that as he turned at the foot of the barren stoop and looked up at the large woman in the door. Then she shut the door.

Activities

1. Work in a group to convert this short story into a play for presentation to the class. Retain the meaning of the original story, using techniques and elements appropriate to drama. Rehearse and present the play.

2. Using either video, audio, or print, develop an advertising campaign to discourage young people from turning to crime. Use Mrs. Luella Bates Washington Jones and Roger as your "poster people."

3. Imagine that you are Roger ten years after the story has ended. Write a diary entry explaining what has happened in your life since the incident with Mrs. Jones, and how that event changed you.

4. As Roger, write a letter to Mrs. Jones telling her what you were thinking but couldn't say at the time.

Your Hidden Skills

TG MAGAZINE

Focus Your Learning
Reading this article will help you:
- analyse how information is presented
- develop criteria for effective presentation
- create a media work

Do you think you're too compulsive? Too loud? Too sensitive? Do teachers accuse you of talking too much? Do your parents tell you you're lazy?

Here's a surprising fact. What you think is a major fault could be a strength and just what employers need to get the job done.

If you think you are ...

Too compulsive:
Your friends think you're nuts because everything in your locker is in alphabetical order.

Too argumentative:
You always tell people exactly what you think and feel—even if it's about them!

Too lazy:
You always start essays the night before they're due. If there's a reason not to do something, you'll find it.

Too loud:
When you talk, people can't help but hear you—you love being the centre of attention.

Too stubborn:
You hate to back down and don't like to admit when you're wrong.

Too talkative:
No one can get a word in when you're in the conversation—you *are* the conversation!

Too weird:
You dance to a different beat and do things your own way.

Then say this to an employer ...

Too compulsive?
I have strong organizational skills and an ability to plan ahead. I always do a thorough job.

Too argumentative?
I'm very confident and deal with issues directly.
I enjoy taking on a challenge.

Too lazy?
I can work with short deadlines and under pressure.

Too loud?
I'm enthusiastic and outgoing. I interact easily with groups.

Too stubborn?
I'm persistent. I always carry a project through to the end.

Too talkative?
I'm articulate and enjoy public speaking.
I'm persuasive and present my ideas well.

Too weird?
I'm innovative and can always offer a fresh perspective. I enjoy taking the initiative.

If you think you are ...

Too indifferent:
You never seem to have a strong opinion and just can't get excited about anything.

Too sensitive:
You take everything to heart.

Too serious:
Everything is important. You never seem to relax.

Too extreme:
You always overreact—every event in your life seems to be out of a soap opera.

Too shy:
Meeting new people makes you really nervous—you end up doing most things alone.

Then say this to an employer ...

Too indifferent?
I'm adaptable and can be counted on to stay calm in stressful situations.

Too sensitive?
I'm a caring, perceptive person with strong people skills and a desire to please others.

Too serious?
I'm a careful and reliable person. I'm good at considering all the options.

Too extreme?
I'm imaginative. My creativity leads to good ideas.

Too shy?
I'm self-motivated. I work well independently and need little supervision.

Activities

1. How is the information in this article organized? How effective is the layout?

2. Work with a partner to develop a set of criteria for an effective visual layout. Use this article, as well as samples from magazines. Share your criteria with the class and come to a consensus on a class set of criteria.

3. Create a new layout for this article. Use the class-developed criteria to assess your final product.

The Tell-Tale Heart

EDGAR ALLAN POE

True!—Nervous—very, very dreadfully nervous I had been and am; but why *will* you say that I am mad? The disease has sharpened my senses—not destroyed—not dulled them. Above all was the sense of hearing acute. I heard all things in the heaven and in the earth, I heard many things in hell. How, then, am I mad? Hearken! And observe how healthily—how calmly I can tell you the whole story.

It is impossible to say how first the idea entered my brain; but once conceived, it haunted me day and night. Object there was none. Passion there was none. I loved the old man. He had never wronged me. He had never given me insult. For his gold I had no desire. I think it was his eye! Yes, it was this! One of his eyes resembled that of a vulture—a pale blue eye, with a film over it. Whenever it fell upon me, my blood ran cold; and so by degrees—very gradually—I made up my mind to take the life of the old man, and thus rid myself of the eye forever.

Now this is the point. You fancy me mad. Madmen know nothing. But you should have seen *me.* You should have seen how wisely I proceeded—with what caution—with what foresight—with what dissimulation I went to work! I was never kinder to the old man than during the whole week before I killed him. And every night, about midnight, I turned the latch of his door and opened it—oh, so gently! And then, when I had made an opening sufficient for my head, I put in a dark lantern, all closed, closed, so that no light shone out, and then I thrust in my head. Oh, you would have laughed to see how cunningly I thrust it in! I moved it slowly—very, very slowly, so that I might not disturb the old man's sleep. It took me an hour to place my whole head within the opening so far that I could see him as he lay upon his bed. Ha! Would a madman have been so wise as this? And then, when my head was well in the room, I undid the lantern cautiously—oh, so cautiously—cautiously (for the hinges creaked)—I undid it just so much that a single thin ray fell upon the vulture eye. And this I did for seven long nights—every night just at midnight—but I found the eye always closed; and so it was impossible to do the work; for it was not the old man who vexed me, but his Evil Eye. And every morning, when the day broke, I went boldly into the chamber, and spoke courageously to him, calling him by name in a hearty tone, and inquiring how he had passed the night. So you see he would have been a very profound old man, indeed, to suspect that every night, just at twelve, I looked in upon him while he slept.

Upon the eighth night I was more than usually cautious in opening the door. A watch's minute hand moves more quickly than did mine. Never before that night had I *felt* the extent of my own powers—of my sagacity. I could scarcely contain my feelings of triumph. To think that there I was, opening the door, little by little, and he not even to dream of my secret deeds or thoughts. I fairly chuckled at the idea; and perhaps he heard me; for he moved on the bed suddenly, as if startled. Now you may think that I drew back—but no. His room was as black as pitch with the thick darkness (for the shutters were close fastened, through fear of robbers), and so I knew that he could not see the opening of the door, and I kept pushing it on steadily, steadily.

I had my head in, and was about to open the lantern, when my thumb slipped upon the tin fastening, and the old man sprang up in the bed, crying out—"Who's there?"

I kept quite still and said nothing. For a whole hour I did not move a muscle, and in the meantime I did not hear him lie down. He was still sitting up in the bed listening—just as I have done, night after night, hearkening to the deathwatches in the wall.

Presently I heard a slight groan, and I knew it was the groan of mortal terror. It was not a groan of pain or of grief—oh, no!—it was the low stifled sound that arises from the bottom of the soul when overcharged with awe. I knew the sound well. Many a night, just at midnight, when all the world slept, it has welled up from my own bosom, deepening, with its dreadful echo, the terrors that distracted me. I say I knew it well. I knew what the old man felt, and pitied him, although I chuckled at heart. I knew that he had been lying awake ever since the first slight noise, when he had turned in the bed. His fears had been ever since growing upon him. He had been trying to fancy them causeless, but could not. He had been saying to himself—"It is nothing but the wind in the chimney—it is only a mouse crossing the floor," or "it is merely a cricket which has made a single chirp." Yes, he has been trying to comfort himself with these suppositions; but he had found all in vain. *All in vain;* because Death, in approaching him, had stalked with his black shadow before him, and enveloped the victim. And it was the mournful influence of the unperceived shadow that caused him to feel—although he neither saw nor heard—to *feel* the presence of my head within the room.

When I had waited a long time, very patiently, without hearing him lie down, I resolved to open a little—a very, very little crevice in the lantern. So I opened it—you cannot imagine how stealthily,

stealthily—until, at length, a single dim ray, like the thread of a spider, shot from out the crevice and fell upon the vulture eye.

It was open—wide, wide open—and I grew furious as I gazed upon it. I saw it with perfect distinctness—all a dull blue, with a hideous veil over it that chilled the very marrow in my bones; but I could see nothing else of the old man's face or person; for I had directed the ray as if by instinct, precisely upon the damned spot.

And now have I not told you that what you mistake for madness is but over-acuteness of the senses? Now, I say, there came to my ears a low, dull, quick sound, such as a watch makes when enveloped in cotton. I knew *that* sound well too. It was the beating of the old man's heart. It increased my fury, as the beating of a drum stimulates the soldier into courage.

But even yet I refrained and kept still. I scarcely breathed. I held the lantern motionless. I tried how steadily I could maintain the ray upon the eye. Meantime the hellish tattoo of the heart increased. It grew quicker and quicker, and louder and louder every instant. The old man's terror *must* have been extreme! It grew louder, I say, louder every moment! Do you mark me well? I have told you that I am nervous: so I am. And now at the dead hour of the night, amid the dreadful silence of that old house, so strange a noise as this excited me to uncontrollable terror. Yet, for some minutes longer I refrained and stood still. But the beating grew louder, louder! I thought the heart must burst. And now a new anxiety seized me—the sound would be heard by a neighbour! The old man's hour had come! With a loud yell, I threw open the lantern and leaped into the room. He shrieked once— once only. In an instant I dragged him to the floor, and pulled the heavy bed over him. I then smiled gaily, to find the deed so far done. But, for many minutes, the heart beat on with a muffled sound. This, however, did not vex me; it would not be heard through the wall. At length it ceased. The old man was dead. I removed the bed and examined the corpse. Yes, he was stone, stone dead. I placed my hand upon the heart and held it there many minutes. There was no pulsation. He was stone dead. His eye would trouble me no more.

If still you think me mad, you will think so no longer when I describe the wise precautions I took for the concealment of the body. The night waned, and I worked hastily, but in silence. First of all I dismembered the corpse. I cut off the head and the arms and the legs.

I then took up three planks from the flooring of the chamber, and deposited all between the scantlings. I then replaced the boards so cleverly, so cunningly, that no human eye—not even *his*—could have detected anything wrong. There was nothing to wash out—no stain of any kind—no bloodspot whatever. I had been too wary for that. A tub had caught all—ha! ha!

When I had made an end of these labours, it was four o'clock—still dark as midnight. As the bell sounded the hour, there came a knocking at the street door. I went down to open it with a light heart—for what had I *now* to fear? There entered three men, who introduced themselves, with perfect suavity, as officers of the police. A shriek had been heard by a neighbour during the night; suspicion of foul play had been aroused; information had been lodged at the police office, and they (the officers) had been deputed to search the premises.

I smiled—for *what* had I to fear? I bade the gentlemen welcome. The shriek, I said, was my own in a dream. The old man, I mentioned, was absent in the country. I took my visitors all over the house. I bade them search—search *well*. I led them, at length, to *his* chamber. I showed them his treasures, secure, undisturbed. In the enthusiasm of my confidence, I brought chairs into the room, and desired them *here* to rest from their fatigues, while I myself, in the wild audacity of my perfect triumph, placed my own seat upon the very spot beneath which reposed the corpse of the victim.

The officers were satisfied. My *manner* had convinced them. I was singularly at ease. They sat, and while I answered cheerily, they chatted familiar things. But, ere long, I felt myself getting pale and wished them gone. My head ached, and I fancied a ringing in my ears: but still they sat and still chatted. The ringing became more distinct—it continued and became more distinct: I talked more freely to get rid of the feeling: but it continued and gained definitiveness—until, at length,

I found that the noise was *not* within my ears.

No doubt I now grew *very* pale—but I talked more fluently, and with a heightened voice. Yet the sound increased—and what could I do? It was a *low, dull, quick sound—much such a sound as a watch makes when enveloped in cotton.* I gasped for breath—and yet the officers heard it not. I talked more quickly—more vehemently; but the noise steadily increased. I arose and argued about trifles, in a high key and with violent gesticulations, but the noise steadily increased. Why *would* they not be gone? I paced the floor to and fro with heavy strides, as if excited to fury by the observation of the men—but the noise steadily increased. Oh God! what *could* I do? I foamed—I raved—I swore! I swung the chair upon which I had been sitting, and grated it upon the boards, but the noise arose over all and continually increased. It grew louder—louder—*louder!* And still the men chatted pleasantly, and smiled. Was it possible they heard not? Almighty God!—no, no! They heard!—they suspected!—they *knew!*—they were making a mockery of my horror!—this I thought, and this I think. But anything was better than this agony! Anything was more tolerable than this derision! I could bear those hypocritical smiles no longer! I felt that I must scream or die!—and now—again! hark! louder! louder! louder! *louder!*—

"Villains!" I shrieked, "dissemble no more! I admit the deed!—tear up the planks!—here, here!—it is the beating of his hideous heart!"

Activities

1. As you read, do one of the following activities: either sketch the strong visual images (e.g., the eye, the mad narrator); or make a list of the sounds the narrator wants us to hear as he tells his story.

2. List the narrator's descriptions of himself as the story develops. Find words and phrases he uses to describe his personality and his behaviour. Write a paragraph describing the effect of these descriptions on your reading of the story.

Ragged Sonnet #64

Leonard Nathan

When the great Jim Thorpe*, alone behind
the line of scrimmage guarding against a pass,
saw one coming, spiralling over his head
in perfect parabolic flight, he did not,
as he could have, spoil the play, but turned
to watch the ball caught by the receiver
for a touchdown. And when his coach, red
with stomping rage, shouted from the sidelines,
"Why, Jim, why?"—Thorpe shrugged, looked away
like a patient man driven to explain
the obvious to a fool, and said (shyly,
I think, and with a gesture toward the sky),
"It was so pretty." Back then, we knew
what greatness was by what it would not do.

---

*Jim Thorpe (1886–1953) was a celebrated U.S. athlete
of Native American descent. He excelled in many sports,
among them track, baseball, and football.

Activities

1. Work with a group. Discuss your experiences when a play or performance in sports was outstanding even though it was not technically successful.

2. Imagine you are Jim Thorpe on the day after the game described in the poem. Write a diary entry describing your feelings about the event.

3. Write a letter to the editor of a school or local newspaper, in which you express your agreement or disagreement with the author of the poem on what "greatness" means in sports. Support your point of view with references to the poem, to how we measure greatness in athletes today, and to how different cultures measure greatness in sports and other areas.

Messages Are

Although this masquerades as inspiration, it is actually advertising. To whom would it appeal? What is the message?

Sometimes postcards of a location are like advertisements for that place. What image of Canada is this postcard portraying? How accurate is the portrayal? How many different images of Canada can you imagine?

CANADA

Everywhere!

What are some of the benefits of clubs such as 4-H for their members and for the community? Why do we wear insignias such as badges or buttons that represent these groups?

What type of medicine does Dr. Seuss dispense? Why would a fridge magnet contain a humorous image? Think of other places where funny cartoons or slogans are placed, and why.

The Monkey's Paw

W. W. JACOBS

Moos-O-Men Ivan Eyre

Focus Your Learning

Reading this play will help you to:

- identify effective techniques for creating suspense
- write instructions
- recombine ideas and information to understand more
- explain opinions
- plan and facilitate small-group activities

Characters

Narrator

Herbert White

Mr. White

Sergeant Morris

Mrs. White

Stranger

SCENE 1

Narrator: It is a cold, wet night outside. We are inside a warm, cozy house. A fire is burning brightly in the fireplace. An old man, Mr. White, and his son, Herbert, are playing chess. Mrs. White is knitting by the fire. They are expecting a visitor—Sergeant Morris, who has just come back from India. There is a knock at the door.

Mr. White: There he is. I'll let him in.

Narrator: Mr. White goes to the door and returns with a tall, red-faced man. Sergeant Morris shakes hands with everyone and goes to the fire.

Sergeant Morris: Ah, this feels good! It's really cold outside.

Mr. White: Even with this bad weather, it must be good to get back home to England.

Herbert: I'd love to go to India! It must be interesting. England is so dull. Nothing exciting ever happens here.

Mr. White: Morris, why don't you tell us more about that monkey's paw we've heard about?

Sergeant Morris:	There's nothing to it, really. Just some strange old Eastern magic.
Herbert:	Oh, please tell us! It's a good night for a story.
Sergeant Morris:	Well, it looks just like an ordinary paw. Nothing special about it.
Narrator:	He takes a small paw from his pocket and gives it to Herbert.
Mrs. White:	Ugh! Herbert, how can you touch that awful old thing?
Mr. White:	It sure doesn't look like magic. What's so special about it?
Sergeant Morris:	An old holy man in India put a spell on it. He wanted to show that fate rules people's lives, and that if you mess with fate, you'll get hurt. He put a spell on the paw so that three different men could have three wishes from it.
Mrs. White:	You sound so serious about it! It's just an ugly old paw, after all.
Herbert:	Why don't you make three wishes on it, Sergeant Morris?
Sergeant Morris:	(*looking hard at Herbert*). I have. (*He turns pale at the thought.*)
Mrs. White:	Well, did you really get the three wishes?
Sergeant Morris:	Yes, I did. But let's not talk about it.
Mrs. White:	Has anyone else wished?
Sergeant Morris:	The first man had his three wishes. I don't know what

the first two were. But the third wish was for death. That's how I got the paw.

Herbert: You mean he wished to die, and he did?

Sergeant Morris: Yes.

Mrs. White: So what? It's probably just a coincidence.

Mr. White: I'm not so sure. If you've had your three wishes, why don't you give the paw to someone else?

Sergeant Morris: I thought of selling it, but I don't think I will. It has caused enough trouble already.

Narrator: Sergeant Morris picks up the paw and throws it on the logs burning in the fireplace.

Mr. White: Don't do that! (*He snatches the paw from the fire.*) Sergeant Morris, if you don't want the paw, then give it to me.

Sergeant Morris: Take it. But you're a fool if you do. And don't blame me for what happens. Listen, be sensible. Burn it.

Mr. White: No. I want it. How do you make the wishes?

Sergeant Morris: Hold it up in your right hand and wish aloud. But I warn you of the result.

Narrator: Mrs. White gets up to make dinner.

Mrs. White: Why don't you wish for four pairs of hands for me?

Sergeant Morris: If you *must* wish, wish for something sensible. But I think you'll be sorry.

Narrator: The monkey's paw was forgotten during dinner. For the rest of the evening the Whites listened to Sergeant Morris talk about India.

Sergeant Morris: My goodness, it's late. I've talked too much. I must be going. But before I leave, I wish you'd throw the monkey's paw away.

Mrs. White: Don't worry, Sergeant. We'll be careful.

Narrator: Sergeant Morris puts on his coat, says goodnight, and walks out the door.

Herbert: (*looking at the paw*). A magic monkey's paw—how silly! Wish to be a king, Father, then Mother can't boss you around.

Mrs. White: (*laughing*). Wish for two hundred pounds to pay off the mortgage.

Mr. White: Why not? Let's try it. (*He holds up the paw in his right hand.*) I wish for two hundred pounds.

Narrator: Suddenly, he drops the paw.

Mr. White: Ahhh! It moved! It twisted like a snake! I swear it did!

Mrs. White: It couldn't have. It's just your imagination.

Herbert: I don't see any money. (*He picks up the paw and puts it on the table.*) I guess it doesn't work.

Mr. White: There's no harm done. But it gave me quite a scare. Now let's go to bed and forget about magic for a while.

SCENE 2

Narrator: Now it is the next morning. The Whites are eating breakfast.

Mrs. White:	Isn't it funny how in the light of day your night fears seem so foolish? That paw is really silly. How could it grant wishes? Even if it could, how could wishes hurt you?
Herbert:	The money could drop on your head.
Mr. White:	That's not how it happens. The wishes are granted so naturally it seems the paw has nothing to do with it. It seems like a coincidence.
Herbert:	Well, save some of the money for me. I've got to get to work. So long.
Narrator:	Herbert goes off to work and the day passes as usual. Later, as it's getting dark, Mr. and Mrs. White sit down to tea.
Mrs. White:	Herbert will have a laugh when he goes home. How could a monkey's paw give us two hundred pounds?
Mr. White:	Well, the paw did move in my hand, like it was alive. I felt it. What's the matter?
Narrator:	Mrs. White does not answer her husband. She is watching a man who is standing at the gate. Finally he comes to the door. As Mrs. White lets him in, she thinks of the two hundred pounds.
Stranger:	I was asked to come here. I'm from Maw and Meggins.
Mrs. White:	Maw and Meggins? That's where Herbert works! Is anything wrong? Has anything happened to him? What is it?
Mr. White:	Now, sit down, Mother. I'm sure he hasn't brought bad news.

Stranger:	I'm sorry—
Mrs. White:	He's hurt! He's hurt, isn't he?
Stranger:	He was badly hurt. But he's not in any pain.
Mrs. White:	Thank goodness! Thank—
Narrator:	She stops when she looks at the man's face. She realizes what he has said. There is an awful silence.
Mr. White:	What—what happened?
Stranger:	He was caught in the machinery. He was killed instantly.
Narrator:	Mr. White takes his wife's hands.
Stranger:	The company wanted me to give you their deep sympathy.
Narrator:	There is no answer. The old woman is pale. Her husband is hardly breathing.
Stranger:	Maw and Meggins wish to give you some money. Your son was a good worker for them.
Narrator:	Mr. White drops his wife's hand. He stares with horror at the Stranger.
Mr. White:	(whispering). How much money?
Stranger:	Two hundred pounds.
Narrator:	Mrs. White screams as Mr. White faints.

SCENE 3

Narrator:	The Whites buried their son in the cemetery three kilometres away. As the days passed, they hardly spoke. They had nothing to talk about except sorrow. It is now a week after the funeral. The old man is awakened at night by his wife.
Mrs. White:	The monkey's paw! The paw!
Mr. White:	Where? What's the matter?
Mrs. White:	I want it! Where is it?
Mr. White:	It's downstairs. But why do you want it?
Mrs. White:	Oh, why didn't I think of it before? It's so easy!
Mr. White:	Think of what? What are you talking about?
Mrs. White:	The other two wishes. We've had only one.
Mr. White:	Wasn't that one enough?
Mrs. White:	No! We'll have one more. Get the paw and wish for Herbert to be alive again.
Mr. White:	My God! You're crazy!
Mrs. White:	No I'm not. Hurry! Get it and wish.
Mr. White:	You don't know what you're saying.
Mrs. White:	The first wish came true. Why not the second?
Mr. White:	It was just a terrible coincidence.
Mrs. White:	Go and get the paw and wish.
Narrator:	Mr. White goes downstairs in the dark. He feels his way

to the table where the monkey's paw lies. He rushes back to the bedroom. His wife's face is terrible to see.

Mrs. White: Hurry! Wish!

Mr. White: It's foolish and wicked. The paw is evil.

Mrs. White: Wish!

Mr. White: (*raising his arm*). I wish my son alive.

Narrator: The paw falls to the floor. Mr. and Mrs. White are silent. They wait until the candle burns out. Then they go back to bed. They can't sleep. A stair creaks. A mouse runs through the wall. Mr. White takes a deep breath. He takes the matches, strikes one, and goes downstairs for another candle. At the foot of the stairs the match goes out. There is a quiet knock at the front door. Mr. White doesn't dare breathe. The knock comes again. He turns and runs back to the bedroom. A loud knock sounds through the house.

Mrs. White: What's that noise?

Mr. White: It's a rat. Just a rat.

Mrs. White: No, its Herbert! It's my son!

Narrator: She runs to the door. Mr. White stops her.

Mrs. White: Let me go! I forgot the cemetery is three kilometres away. That's what took him so long. I must let him in!

Mr. White: You can't let him in!

Mrs. White: You're afraid of your own son!

Narrator: There is a knock, and another. The old woman breaks free. She runs downstairs. Mr. White hears the chain on the lock rattle.

Mrs. White: The lock is stuck! I can't reach it. Come and help me!

Narrator: Mr. White is on his knees. He is feeling for the paw. If only he can find it before the thing outside gets in! The knocks are coming loud and fast. He hears his wife drag a chair to the door. She climbs on the chair. He hears the bolt creak back. At the same time he finds the paw and holds it in the air.

Mr. White: (*whispering*). I wish my son back in the grave.

Narrator: Suddenly the knocking stops. The door opens. A cold wind rushes up the stairs. A long cry of sorrow from his wife gives Mr. White the courage to run downstairs. He goes out to the gate. The street lamp shines on a quiet, empty road.

Activities

1. List the techniques the author uses to create and build suspense. Imagine that you are the producer of this play. Write some instructions for your actors so that they know how to convey the mood of suspense.

2. Write the story of how the first owner of the paw ended up wishing for death.

3. Write a newspaper editorial expressing the view that Mr. White is or is not responsible for his son's death. Use facts from the story and persuasive language to explain your opinion.

4. Imagine what the characters do with the paw at the end of the play. With two or three others, write the next scene, in which the characters have to get rid of the paw. Practise, revise, and present your scene to the class. Compare the interpretations of different groups. Are some more plausible than others? Why?

How To Hang Up the Telephone

DELIA EPHRON

Focus Your Learning
Reading this dialogue will help you to:
- connect your own experiences with those of others
- create original dialogue
- plan and facilitate small-group activities

"Good-bye."

"'Bye."

"Are you still there?"

"Are you?"

"Yeah. Why didn't you hang up?"

"Why didn't you?"

"I was waiting for you."

"I was waiting for *you*. You go first."

"No, you first."

"No, you first."

"No, you first."

"OK, I know. I'll count to three and we'll both hang up at the same time. Ready? One, two, three, 'bye."

"'Bye." ...

"Are you still there?"

"Yeah."

"Why didn't you?"

"What do you mean, me?"

"OK, do it again. This time for real. One, two, two and a half, two and three quarters, three. 'Bye."

"'Bye."

"Hello."

"Hello."

"Are you still there?"

"Yeah."

Activities

1. Work in a group. Discuss personal experiences similar to the one described in the dialogue.

2. Read and add to the dialogue with your group in a "round robin." Each person, in turn, reads a line of the existing dialogue, then creates new lines of dialogue. You may wish to tape it after you have practised a few times. How long does your dialogue go on? How do you reach a conclusion?

3. Write an original telephone dialogue in which the two people are efficient communicators.

The Hockey Sweater

STORY BY
ROCH CARRIER

ILLUSTRATIONS BY
SHELDON COHEN

Focus Your Learning
Reading this short story will help you to:
- experience a text from French Canada
- write a description and a news report
- participate in a group inquiry
- create and follow a plan
- identify and evaluate information sources

Taken from *The Hockey Sweater* ©1984 Sheldon Cohen: illustrations published by Tundra Books.

The winters of my childhood were long, long seasons. We lived in three places—the school, the church and the skating-rink—but our real life was on the skating-rink. Real battles were won on the skating-rink. Real strength appeared on the skating-rink. The real leaders showed themselves on the skating-rink.

School was a sort of punishment. Parents always want to punish their children and school is their most natural way of punishing us. However, school was also a quiet place where we could prepare for the next hockey game, lay out our next strategies.

As for church, we found there the tranquillity of God: there we forgot school and dreamed about the next hockey game. Through our daydreams it might happen that we would recite a prayer: we would ask God to help us play as well as Maurice Richard.

I remember very well the winter of 1946. We all wore the same uniform as Maurice Richard, the red, white and blue uniform of the Montreal Canadiens, the best hockey team in the world. We all combed our hair like Maurice Richard, and to keep it in place we used a kind of glue—a great deal of glue. We laced our skates like Maurice Richard. We cut his pictures out of all the newspapers. Truly, we knew everything there was to know about him.

On the ice, when the referee blew his whistle the two teams would rush at the puck; we were five Maurice Richards against five other Maurice Richards, throwing themselves on the puck. We were ten players all wearing the uniform of the Montreal Canadiens, all with the same burning enthusiasm. We all wore the famous number 9 on our backs.

How could we forget that!

One day, my Montreal Canadiens sweater was too small for me; and it was ripped in several places. My mother said: "If you wear that old sweater, people are going to think we are poor!"

Then she did what she did whenever we needed new clothes. She started to look through the catalogue that the Eaton company in Montreal sent us in the mail every year. My mother was proud. She

Taken from *The Hockey Sweater* ©1984 Sheldon Cohen: illustrations published by Tundra Books.

never wanted to buy our clothes at the general store. The only clothes that were good enough for us were the latest styles from Eaton's catalogue. My mother did not like the order forms included in the catalogue. They were written in English and she did not understand a single word of it. To order my hockey sweater, she did what she always did. She took out her writing pad and wrote in her fine schoolteacher's hand: "Dear Monsieur Eaton, Would you be so kind as to send me a Canadiens hockey sweater for my son, Roch, who is ten years old and a little bit tall for his age? Docteur Robitaille thinks he is a little too thin. I am sending you three dollars. Please send me the change if there is any. I hope your packing will be better than it was last time."

Monsieur Eaton answered my mother's letter promptly. Two weeks later we received the sweater.

That day I had one of the greatest disappointments of my life! Instead of the red, white and blue Montreal Canadiens sweater, Monsieur Eaton had sent the blue and white sweater of the Toronto Maple Leafs. I had always worn the red, white and blue sweater of the Montreal Canadiens. All my friends wore the red, white and blue sweater. Never had anyone in my village worn the Toronto sweater. Besides, the Toronto team was always being beaten by the Canadiens.

With tears in my eyes, I found the strength to say: "I'll never wear that uniform."

"My boy," said my mother, "first you're going to try it on! If you make up your mind about something before you try it, you won't go very far in this life."

My mother had pulled the blue and white Toronto Maple Leafs sweater over my head and put my arms into the sleeves. She pulled

Taken from *The Hockey Sweater* ©1984 Sheldon Cohen: illustrations published by Tundra Books.

the sweater down and carefully smoothed the maple leaf right in the middle of my chest.

I was crying: "I can't wear that."

"Why not? This sweater is a perfect fit."

"Maurice Richard would never wear it."

"You're not Maurice Richard! Besides, it's not what you put on your back that matters, it's what you put inside your head."

"You'll never make me put in my head to wear a Toronto Maple Leafs sweater."

My mother sighed in despair and explained to me: "If you don't keep this sweater which fits you perfectly I'll have to write to Monsieur Eaton and explain that you don't want to wear the Toronto sweater. Monsieur Eaton understands French perfectly, but he's English and he's going to be insulted because he likes the Maple Leafs. If he's insulted, do you think he'll be in a hurry to answer us? Spring will come before you play a single game, just because you don't want to wear that nice blue sweater."

So, I had to wear the Toronto Maple Leafs sweater.

When I arrived at the skating rink in my blue sweater, all the Maurice Richards in red, white and blue came, one by one, and looked at me. The referee blew his whistle and I went to take my usual position. The coach came over and told me I would be on the second line. A few minutes later the second line was called; I jumped onto the ice. The Maple Leafs sweater weighed on my shoulders like a mountain. The captain came and told me to wait; he'd need me later, on defense.

By the third period I still had not played.

Then one of the defensemen was hit on the nose with a stick and it started to bleed. I jumped onto the ice. My moment had come!

The referee blew his whistle and gave me a penalty. He said there were already five players on the ice. That was too much! It was too unfair! "This is persecution!" I shouted. "It's just because of my blue sweater!"

I crashed my stick against the ice so hard that it broke.

I bent down to pick up the pieces. When I got up, the young curate, on skates, was standing in front of me.

"My child," he said, "just because you're wearing a new Toronto Maple Leafs sweater, it doesn't mean you're going to make the laws around here. A good boy never loses his temper. Take off your skates and go to the church and ask God to forgive you."

Wearing my Maple Leafs sweater I went to the church, where I prayed to God.

I asked God to send me right away, a hundred million moths that would eat up my Toronto Maple Leafs sweater.

Activities

1. What is the setting of this story? Consider time period and physical location. How does the setting contribute to plot, character, and theme?

2. Imagine that you are a writer for the school newspaper who sees the main character on the ice wearing his Maple Leafs sweater. Write the news report, including the headline, that would be on the front cover of the paper.

3. Work with a group. Identify and evaluate the information sources you need in order to create a collage of famous Montreal Canadiens and Toronto Maple Leafs players of the past and present. Create the collage, including informational captions, for classroom display.

Catch SARAH ELLIS

"It's a rite of passage," said my aunt Darlene.

We were sitting in an ice-cream parlour celebrating the fact that I had just passed my driving test.

Darlene raised her Coke float. "Welcome to the adult world. May all your parallel parks be perfect."

I held up a spoonful of hot fudge sundae. "To a good teacher." Darlene was a good teacher, patient and funny. She had taken over my driving instruction from Dad, who got so nervous with me at the wheel that he burped all the time.

"She'll talk your ear off," Dad warned.

She did, a continuous commentary insulting the behaviour of other drivers. It made my nervousness dissolve. I'll take talking over burping any time.

"We just don't have enough rituals for these occasions," said Darlene. "We really need something in this culture—a chant or a dance or some libation to the goddess of the road."

"Ice cream is just fine," I said.

"These passages in our lives are what connect us to the great cycles of existence …"

French vanilla, black raspberry, tropical fruit swirl. Sometimes I don't pay total attention to Darlene. I glanced above the list of flavours to the clock on the wall.

"Hey, Darlene. It's 5:20. We have to go. I have orchestra tonight."

Darlene slurped the last of her drink and then returned the glass to the counter. She stopped to compliment the waitress on her product and her excellent service.

I jiggled on the balls of my feet. Darlene is a great person with no grip on time.

Just as we were heading out the door, an old man spoke to Darlene. He had grey hair and a dirty khaki raincoat, and he was sitting alone.

Darlene stopped. "What's that? I didn't catch what you said."

The man looked up and said, in a cracking voice, "My little king is gone."

Oh, no. I glanced back at the clock. It was really time to go. I tried to catch Darlene's eye, but she was pulling up a chair to sit next to the old man.

"Do you know where he is?"

Dar*lene*, he's one of those mumblers. Come *on*.

The old man shook his head. "He just went away."

"Okay. When did you see him last?"

Why was she having this nutso conversation?

"At the park. I took off his leash and he chased a squirrel."

"So King is your dog?"

The old man nodded and turned away.

Darlene stood up and pushed her chair into the table with a clang. "Come on then. We'll look for him."

"Darlene," I half whispered. "My rehearsal. I have to be leaving from home in twenty minutes."

"Rita, this man has lost his dog. We have priorities here."

The old man didn't walk very well, so Darlene put him in the front seat of the car and we set off into rush-hour traffic. Up streets and down alleys. Darlene talked a mile a minute and the old man said nothing. I cranked open the back seat window to let out the musty, sharp, old-man smell.

Half an hour and several illegal left-hand turns later, we found the dog—a lanky, hairy, off-white mutt nosing in a garbage can. The old man barely waited for the car to stop before he was out the door. Darlene watched him hugging the dog for a few seconds and then we drove away.

By the time we escaped from the snarl of traffic and were on the road home we were nearly an hour late and everything was making me furious. I was furious at the stupid ugly dog for running away. I was furious at the smelly old man who didn't even say thank you. I was furious at Darlene for getting involved. I sat in the corner of the back seat and chewed on my fury. I *hate* being late.

Mum and Dad were out when we got back home. Darlene came in with me and asked if it would help if she fixed me some supper.

"Supper! I don't even have time to get there now. I've missed the bus and they only run every forty-five minutes. I *can't* miss this rehearsal. It's the last one before the Christmas concert."

"Oh, honey, I would drive you but I've got my realignment class tonight." Darlene explained her realignment class to me once. They realign something, their spines or the universe. "Hang on! I've got it. I'll get a ride with someone and you can borrow my car."

"Alone?"

"Sure, you've got a license. Why not?"

I glanced at the clock. There was no time to make this decision. I took a deep breath. "Sure. Thanks."

I grabbed my oboe and music and ran out to the car. It felt very big and lonely as I slid inside. I adjusted the seat and both mirrors. I figured out the headlights and where the high beams were, in case a dark country road should suddenly appear between my house and the arts centre. I put my hands at ten o'clock and two o'clock and set off.

I drove just under the speed limit, and cars kept coming up close behind and swerving around in a snarly way. I tried one of Darlene's lines. "Don't waste those valuable micro-seconds, buddy." It wasn't that helpful. At night, when you can't see the drivers, cars seem alive, like wild animals in the jungle.

When I arrived at the arts centre there was no time to search for parking on the street, so I pulled into the underground lot. It was very full. Must have been some concert on. Four minutes. I corkscrewed down and down and the car clock seemed to speed up.

Finally I found a space. It took me three tries to back the car between a van and a pillar. I grabbed my oboe case and squeezed out the door sideways, grateful that I didn't play the cello. I ran through the rows of cars to the elevator, caught it just as the door was closing, slid up to the music school, sprinted to the rehearsal room and plunked down in my seat three minutes late.

I slipped off my jacket and started to put together my oboe. My nose began to drip. As I leaned forward to get a Kleenex from my jacket pocket, I knocked the music stand. It started to tip and Yvette, my stand partner, caught it and set it back in place, very precisely. She gave me a little pitying smile. She looked cool and perfect as usual. Yvette probably has a special drip-free nose to go with her zit-free complexion. I wanted to kick her.

Behind me, Claude, who plays English horn, was sucking his reed very enthusiastically. It was a loud, wet, slurpy sound. I wanted to kick him, too.

Mr. Farland stepped up to the podium and raised his eyebrows. "Quite settled, Rita? Then let's begin. Now that we've got all the double reeds here, why don't we start with the Bach?"

Mr. Farland had done an arrangement for oboes, English horns and bassoons from Bach's "Art of the Fugue." Before we had played it for the first time he had given us a long lecture, all about counterpoint and mirror fugues and canons. I understood the first part okay, how fugues are like rounds or catches, like "Row, row, row your boat." ("You'll be chasing each other," said Mr. Farland.) But then his explanation got very complicated and the whole thing sounded like mathematical snoresville to me.

Snoresville until we played it, that is. Even that first time, with its squeaks and blats and total breakdown halfway through, I knew I was going to love being inside this music.

We had practised a lot and I thought it was ready to go. But something happened that night. Mr. Farland counted us in and the oboes started. We sounded plain and small. Then the English horns took over the melody and we hovered above them. But the best moment came when the bassoons entered below us all. It was like being lifted up by a giant warm wind, our chairs levitated off the floor.

All my leftover fury and the tension of the jungle drive dissolved, and I felt as though my oboe was a part of my body, its sound my voice. And it wasn't just me. I heard parts of the melody above and below me, before and after me, and I felt the gentle tug of all the lines of sound, a web.

Yvette with her attitude, gross Claude, grumpy me—even

sarcastic Mr. Farland and some composer who's been dead for two hundred and fifty years—we were all connected.

When we finished, Jamal, the first bassoonist, punched the air with his fist—"Yes!"—and we all laughed. I laughed because I had to let the bigness out.

"That was terrific," said Mr. Farland. "You really reminded us that you are *wind* instruments. Whatever you did tonight, bottle it for the concert."

The rest of the rehearsal was fine, and the Bach was playing inside me when we finished and I headed back to the car. But when I got off the elevator, Bach vanished as I stared at the two opposite glass doors leading out into the lot and realized I had no idea where the car was. I closed my eyes and tried to remember which way I had come. It was no use. It had vanished in the panic of my arrival.

I took a chance on the left door. How many rows of cars had I run by? And from which direction?

The parking lot was very quiet, except for that big-building hum. It was humming in the key of D. Many of the cars were gone. Spaces appeared like missing teeth. I held my music case a bit tighter and decided on a methodical approach. I would walk down each row.

Minutes later I heard the first squeal, a perfect minor chord. Then three more squeals and a car pulled up just behind me. It slowed down.

"Hey! Want a ride to your car?"

I didn't look. "No, thank you." I kept on walking. Calmly, not speeding up.

"Aw, come on. Why don't you want a ride? We've got treats in here. Don't you want to see?"

The car kept pace with me, just behind me as I walked, and I started to get a pounding in my ears. I tried to think of the fastest way back to the elevator.

I ducked into the next row. I heard the car squeal around the corner, and it came towards me as I came out from behind a pillar. This time I saw them. Three men in a black convertible.

It was another voice. "I don't think she likes us. Why don't you like us, little girl?"

"I think she's a stuck-up brat, that's what I think. I think we need to teach her a lesson."

Oh, please let there be another noise, of another car, or of footsteps. Why didn't someone come? But there was only the hum and the voices and my heart beating in my ears.

I started to run, weaving in and out of cars. My shoes slapped on the white floor. My shoulder caught the side of a truck and I spun around. The squealing sound was continuous, like an animal being slaughtered, and I couldn't tell what direction it was coming from.

And then Darlene's car appeared. I fumbled for the keys in my purse. The squealing was louder, and a voice echoed through the bright, shadowless light, "What is this, hide and seek?"

The key trembled in the lock and then I was in. I turned the key in the ignition and the engine coughed once and died. I tried to breathe and to remember Darlene's instructions. Pump the gas pedal three times.

And then the convertible was there. In front of my car. Trapping me. The three men got out and in that second I wondered if my back doors were locked. I was frozen in the seat. I couldn't turn around to look.

There was a crash as a beer bottle hit the pillar beside me. I stared at the brown liquid trickling down the whiteness. Then the car began to rock. I looked in the rear-view mirror. Two men were on the trunk, jumping. I could only see legs.

Where was the third man? I twisted around in my seat. The back door on the passenger side was not locked. I started to reach for it when I heard the door click open. I pulled back sharply. Something was squeezing my lungs.

And then a beam of light came in the windshield. I saw a small grey-haired man dressed in a green coverall. He was carrying a cell phone and a big flashlight. He spoke into the phone. "Section E-3. Section E-3, police emergency."

The three men scrambled out from the back, yelling. They shoved the green man aside and jumped into their car. They squealed away.

I had to get out, outside, above ground. Pump the gas pedal three times and wait five seconds. But my right foot was dancing wildly and my leg would not obey me. I leaned into the steering wheel and sobbed. When I looked up there was nobody around. I took a deep breath and made myself remember how to drive.

I circled my way up to the pay booth, telling myself out loud how to do it. When I got there the gate was smashed. There was a police car with a flashing red light and two dogs in the back. A policewoman started to ask me questions, but when she saw how much I was shaking she went and got a blanket to put around me.

"I'm just glad that security guard turned up," I said.

"Hold it," said the parking lot guy. "We don't have security guards."

"I guess it was just a helpful citizen," said the policewoman.

They phoned home and Mum and Dad came to get me.

I stayed home from school the next day. Darlene came over and gave me soup and a foot massage. She made me tell the story quite a few times. Then she made me go driving with her, even though I had decided to shred my license and stick to buses for the rest of my life.

The concert was the next week. As we fell silent after tuning up and the house lights went down, I noticed three latecomers hurrying into the second row. It was Mum, Dad and Darlene. They had come together because Darlene's car was in the shop getting the dents bashed out. Darlene was wearing a red off-the-shoulder sequined dress. She gave me a finger wave. I smiled back. I bet she had made them late. I bet Dad was burping.

The concert went well. The Bach, which we played just before the intermission, was fine. All the notes were right and we didn't drag and nobody squeaked. But our chairs stayed on the floor. Whatever it was that night didn't make it into the bottles.

After the concert there was hot apple juice and gingerbread in the lobby. Mum got all teary the way she does. Dad got cornered by a whiny woman complaining about the Christmas carol medley. Why had we played all those carols nobody had heard of? What happened to "Silent Night"? I turned my back and kept a low profile. Darlene joined them, so I kept on eavesdropping. Darlene is more than a match for any whiner.

"Don't you think that it is significant that it is a proven scientific fact that music rearranges our mental syntax, making us much more open to the positive forces of the universe? I find that especially important as we approach the shortest day of the year. I mean, especially if you're phototropic like I am ..."

I snuck a peek. The whiner was looking hunted and edging away.

As we prepared to leave, Darlene said, "Philip, why don't you just go get the car and pick us up at the front door." She flexed one high-heeled foot. "My shoes hurt." Dad rolled his eyes but he went. Mum kept him company.

I squeezed Darlene's skinny arm. Sometimes she knows things that other people don't, like how a person could really not want to go into the underground parking garage, even with three other people.

We went outside and Darlene lit a cigarette. "I've been thinking about something. You know the security guard that helped you that night? What did he look like?"

"Darlene, I've told you a bunch of times. Short, sort of strong-looking, grey hair, wrinkled forehead and dressed in one of those jumpsuit things that mechanics wear, green."

Darlene nodded. "Yeah, that would be the old guy from the ice-cream place."

"What?"

"You know, the one who lost his dog. Did you recognize him?"

"No, but ... I don't remember what the dog man looked like, and the man in the parking lot, I hardly looked at him. First there was the bright light and then he just disappeared."

Darlene nodded. "Yes, he did what he came to do."

"But that would be an incredible coincidence. I mean, why would he be there in the parking lot at that moment?"

"Oh, honey, he just knew he had to be there to take care of you. He's obviously one of the others, not one of us. But we're all connected."

I stared at Darlene as she took a long drag on her cigarette. One of the others. I hadn't heard about "the others." I suspected I was going to, probably right after the next puff. It would only take one question. The ancient power of ritual, the realignment of the cosmos, the healing effects of music, the interconnection of all things on the planet—Darlene wasn't one to keep the good news to herself.

The car pulled up. The passenger door swung open. I grabbed Darlene's hand and pulled her in after me.

Activities

1. In a two-column chart, write side-by-side character sketches of Darlene and Rita. How do the two characters compare with each other?

2. Imagine that you are Darlene. Write and perform for the class a one-minute dramatic monologue in which you tell Rita about "the others."

3. Work with a group. List and discuss reasons why the author chose the title "Catch," making specific references to the text. Decide if it is an effective choice. Suggest alternative titles.

Ambush

TIM O'BRIEN

Red Sea Louisa Chase

When she was nine, my daughter Kathleen asked if I had ever killed anyone.

She knew about the war; she knew I'd been a soldier. "You keep writing these war stories," she said, "so I guess you must've killed somebody." It was a difficult moment, but I did what seemed right, which was to say, "Of course not," and then to take her onto my lap and hold her for a while. Someday, I hope, she'll ask again. But here I want to pretend she's a grown-up. I want to tell her exactly what happened, or what I remember happening, and then I want to say to her that as a little girl she was absolutely right. This is why I keep writing war stories:

He was a short, slender young man of about twenty. I was afraid of him—afraid of something—and as he passed me on the trail I threw a grenade that exploded at his feet and killed him.

Or to go back:

Shortly after midnight we moved into the ambush site outside My Khe. The whole platoon was there, spread out in the dense brush along the trail, and for five hours nothing at all happened. We were working in two-man teams—one man on

guard while the other slept, switching off every two hours—and I remember it was still dark when Kiowa shook me awake for the final watch. The night was foggy and hot. For the first few moments I felt lost, not sure about directions, groping for my helmet and weapon. I reached out and found three grenades and lined them up in front of me; the pins had already been straightened for quick throwing. And then for maybe half an hour I kneeled there and waited. Very gradually, in tiny slivers, dawn began to break through the fog, and from my position in the brush I could see ten or fifteen metres up the trail. The mosquitoes were fierce. I remember slapping at them, wondering if I should wake up Kiowa and ask for some repellent, then thinking it was a bad idea, then looking up and seeing the young man come out of the fog. He wore black clothing and rubber sandals and a grey ammunition belt. His shoulders were slightly stooped, his head cocked to the side as if listening for something. He seemed at ease. He carried his weapon in one hand, muzzle down, moving without any hurry up the centre of the trail. There was no sound at all—none that I can remember. In a way, it seemed, he was part of the morning fog, or my own imagination, but there was also the reality of what was happening in my stomach. I had already pulled the pin on a grenade. I had come up to a crouch. It was entirely automatic. I did not hate the young man; I did not see him as the enemy; I did not ponder issues of morality or politics or military duty. I crouched and kept my head low. I tried to swallow whatever was rising from my stomach, which tasted like lemonade, something fruity and sour. I was terrified. There were no thoughts about killing. The grenade was to make him go away—just evaporate—and I leaned back and felt my mind go empty and then felt it fill up again. I had already thrown the grenade before telling myself to throw it. The brush was thick and I had to lob it high, not aiming, and I remember the grenade seeming to freeze above me for an instant, as if a camera had clicked, and I remember ducking down and holding my breath and seeing little wisps of fog rise from the earth. The grenade bounced once and rolled across the trail. I did not hear it, but there must've been a sound, because the young man dropped his weapon and began to run, just two or three quick steps, then he hesitated, swivelling to his right, and he glanced down at the grenade and tried to cover his head but never did. It occurred to me then that he was about to die. I wanted to warn him. The grenade made a popping noise—not soft but not loud either—not what I'd expected—and there was a puff of dust and smoke—a small white puff—and the young man seemed to jerk upward as if pulled by invisible wires. He fell on his back. His rubber sandals had been blown off. There was no wind. He lay at the centre of the trail, his right leg bent beneath him, his one eye shut, his other eye a huge star-shaped hole.

It was not a matter of live or die. There was no real peril. Almost certainly the young man would have passed by. And it will always be that way.

Later, I remember, Kiowa tried to tell me that the man would've died anyway. He told me that it was a good kill, that I was a soldier and this was a war, that I should shape up and stop staring and ask myself what the dead man would've done if things were reversed.

None of it mattered. The words seemed far too complicated. All I could do was gape at the fact of the young man's body.

Even now I haven't finished sorting it out. Sometimes I forgive myself, other times I don't. In the ordinary hours of life I try not to dwell on it, but now and then, when I'm reading a newspaper or just sitting alone in a room, I'll look up and see the young man coming out of the morning fog. I'll watch him walk toward me, his shoulders slightly stooped, his head cocked to the side, and he'll pass within a few yards of me and suddenly smile at some secret thought and then continue up the trail to where it bends back into the fog.

Activities

1. Set up a formal debate, with one team arguing that the narrator's actions were right, the other team that they were wrong. Invite some impartial guests to evaluate the debate.

2. Work with a partner. Imagine that you are the narrator ten years from now and that you must tell your daughter the truth. Discuss exactly what you will say to her and in what form (e.g., orally in conversation, written in a letter, etc.).

At School

A School Scene Mir Sayyid-Ali

Focus Your Learning
Studying this painting will help you:
- develop questions to extend understanding
- appreciate the artistry of the image

Activities

1. Examine this painting carefully to identify what each character in the picture is doing. Develop questions that various characters might have for each other. For example, the man at the top of the picture might be asking, "What constellations do you see in the sky?"

2. Imagine the viewpoint of the artist. Can he really see all of the rooms in the school at once? Explain why he uses this perspective.

1. Work with a partner. First, each of you creates a graphic organizer comparing the characters of Mrs. Jones in "Thank You, Ma'am" and Aunt Darlene in "Catch." Then, compare and evaluate the type of organizer each of you has created and the information it includes. What changes would you make to your organizers after comparing them? Would a different type of organizer work even better? If so, create one with your partner.

2. Work with a small group. Begin by discussing the theme of "Ragged Sonnet #64." Next, develop a collage that illustrates the theme of the poem, keeping a record of your reasons for choosing particular images and words to include in the work. Present your collage to the class. Be prepared to explain and defend your choice of images and words.

3. Work with a partner. Choose the selection in this section that affected you most. Write the first draft of a review explaining why you felt so strongly about the selection and why you would recommend it to others. Share this draft with your partner and help each other edit. Write a final draft of your review and present it orally to the class.

4. Work with a small group. Choose the three selections in this section that you think have the most unusual situations or endings. Discuss what is unusual about them and how their authors use particular techniques and elements to achieve this. Choose a situation or ending from one of these three to dramatize for the class. Develop a short script for the dramatization, or mime the situation or ending.

5. Work with a small group. Review all the selections in this section in the light of the following two themes: "Challenges and Teamwork" and "Dreams and Reality." Discuss which selections belong in which category. Do any belong in both? Record your reasons on a chart and present them to the class. After listening to the reasons presented by other groups, review your own with your group. Discuss any changes that you would make based on what you heard from the other groups.

6. Imagine that this section was being published as a separate book. Would you choose one of the visuals included in the section for a cover? If so, which one and why? If not, which of the selections would you use as an inspiration for a cover? What specific image or idea would you illustrate from that selection? Why? Describe the illustration that you have in mind.

look closely

2

What lies beneath the surface of your life?

Analysing hidden depths starts with taking things apart. Then you can reassemble them—and understand them—in a new way. So focus your mental telescope…and look closely.

The Cool Crowd

PHYLLIS HERSH
KEATON

Focus Your Learning
Reading this article will
help you to:
- connect your own
  experiences to those
  of others
- create original text
- plan and facilitate a
  group presentation
- evaluate group
  procedures
- distinguish between
  the techniques of first-
  person and third-
  person writing
- express and explain
  personal points of
  view

Sabrina, fifteen, was just hanging out with her friends, laughing and telling jokes as usual. But some of the guys started making fun of the new boy she was dating. The jokes turned cruel. Sabrina knew Brian was different from her crowd, but she really liked him. He had his own way of looking at things, and spending time with him was fun. Should she quit seeing him? Or should she stand up for him?

Problems like Sabrina's result from the very nature of cliques. A clique is an exclusive crowd of teens who have many of the same interests. The key word is *exclusive,* but not in the sense of "special"; cliques *exclude* people who do not fit in. Cliques may not be "nice," but these crowds serve a purpose for the people in them.

Teens face tremendous physical and mental changes. It helps to know that these changes are normal. When friends speak, dress, and act the same way, it helps them feel good about themselves. Cliques reinforce those positive feelings. The negative side is that people who do not speak, dress, and act the same are left out. And some clique members feel better about themselves by shutting others out.

"We Say Who Sits Here"

One day Thea, thirteen, was eating lunch with Sarah and some other kids in her crowd. Then Amanda brought her tray to the table. Amanda and Thea were working on a project together and just starting to be friends.

Sarah said, "Hey, you can't sit here! This is our table, and we say who sits here and who doesn't."

Amanda's face fell. Thea could tell Sarah had really hurt her. Sarah was Thea's best friend, but Thea didn't like what she was doing to Amanda.

Thea said, "Amanda can sit here if she wants to."

Then Sarah turned on Thea. "If you want to sit with Amanda, do it at another table."

Thea had only a few seconds to choose. Should she go along to get along with Sarah and the others? Or should she do what she thinks is right?

Making Choices

Learning to deal with a clique—deciding when to go along with the group and when to follow your own feelings—is part of growing up.

In the case of Sarah and Amanda, Thea faced a conflict. Sarah wanted to keep Amanda out of the group. The two had very different personalities, and Sarah saw Amanda as a threat. So Sarah treated her badly. Putting someone else down gives some people a feeling of power. It hides their own lack of self-esteem.

But Thea told Sarah, "Amanda and I are staying here. If you don't like it, you can go sit somewhere else." Sarah and the others moved to another table. But later, they apologized to Thea and Amanda.

Thea felt good about herself and was able to make her point without being dropped by her group.

For Sabrina, things were a little different. She got angry at her friends and walked away. She went for days without speaking to them. She really didn't know if she wanted to be part of the group anymore. Her interests were changing, and she really didn't *need* her crowd as much as she had just a year before. Maybe it was time to make new friends.

Getting Shut Out

Thea and Sabrina both made choices. But many people don't have the option of *choosing* whether or not to be part of a group. The crowd makes it clear it doesn't want *them*. In fact, almost everyone has been shut out by a clique at one time or another. And that can hurt.

"Those who are rejected by cliques may become upset, depressed, and form a poor self-concept," says Susan Forman, a psychology professor at the University of South Carolina. "Some resent the clique and become vindictive. But those who have been rejected may find friendship in other groups."

Owen was recently shut out. He'd always been friends with Bobby, Mark, and their crowd. But Bobby and Mark got better and better at sports, and Owen was no jock. Then Bobby told Owen he didn't want to hang out with him after baseball games. Owen felt hurt. Bobby and Mark were part of the crowd of jocks and cheerleaders, and now Owen wasn't.

Mark underlined the point one day when he made fun of Owen's Metallica T-shirt. "You think you're so tough!" Mark said, pointing at the T-shirt. "I bet you don't even know the words to their songs."

"You want me to sing them for you now?" Owen said, looking around uncomfortably at the guys who had once been his friends.

Bobby and some others began poking fun at Owen, too. Owen had never felt as bad in his life.

Turning Things Around

Owen didn't know what to do when he lost his old friends. At first, he moped around school and stayed in his room at home. Later, he started spending afternoons by himself skateboarding. He began hanging around a local skateboard shop to pick up some tips. There he met a few other guys who were into skateboards. Being with them helped him feel better about himself. It also made Owen think about what was important to him and understand himself better. And he figured out that no matter how bleak life may seem, things can change.

Both Thea and Owen turned bad experiences into good ones. They learned skills they will be able to use again and again—because cliques are not just a problem for teens. Adults who move to new communities or start new jobs know that there may be people who try to exclude them.

So what do you do if you have a problem with a clique? It might be tempting to sleep until it's over. But, says Stephanie Impellitiere, a guidance counsellor at Garrison (NY) Union Free School, the way to get your way in a clique is to assert yourself. "Listen to what's going on in the group," she says. "Then be assertive about what you want."

One reason that Thea was able to get what she wanted—making a new friend *and* staying in the group—was that she reacted strongly to what Sarah told Amanda. And she let the others know exactly how she felt. If she had gone along, Sarah would have taken her silence as approval of her behaviour. Thea found a positive way to deal with the problem.

Finally, it's important to keep communication lines open. "If you are having a problem," says Impellitiere, "tell someone about it. Share your story with a friend in or outside your clique or with your parents or a teacher." They may be able to help you get perspective.

How Cliques Tick

It's a need to matter to others that makes cliques tick. According to Gerald Adams, program director of Research Lab for Adolescence at the University of Utah, cliques generally begin in late elementary school. The groups usually include boys or girls, but not both. In junior high, these crowds begin to mix. As teens get older, the groups break into true cliques made up of people with similar interests and economic backgrounds. But during the late high school years, the groups may begin to lose some of their power as teens begin to pair off. Then the stage is set for dating and establishing adult friendships.

Cliques often do serve a purpose. The groups "sort out" kids and teach them what others think is socially acceptable, says Adams. Having a peer group that sets rules can help kids make the transition from being a child in a family with rules to being an independent adult.

Some things about cliques are not obvious, says Stephanie Impellitiere, and dealing with them is easier when you understand how they work. Things to remember:

- Cliques are made up of people with a common bond that is not always stated. For example, people with alcoholic

parents may be attracted to each other, even though they are unaware that they share the same problem.

- There is a leader in a clique, whether or not other members say so. Trouble occurs when another crowd member attempts to take over.

- People in cliques have a strong need to be accepted. Going along with certain behaviour may be the only way to gain acceptance by the group. This can lead to trouble in some cases, but it is not always bad. The groups can help people understand their limits and learn to deal with others.

Activities

1. Work with a small group. List and discuss your experiences with cliques and cliquishness. Choose one of the experiences to present as a dramatic scene. Write, rehearse, revise, and present the scene. Afterwards, evaluate the presentation with your group.

2. Choose one of the scenarios described in this article. Rewrite the scenario as a

first-person journal entry written by one of the people involved.

3. Work with a small group. Using your own ideas and specific examples from the article, informally debate the statement: "Cliques are valuable in today's society."

See Saw

(EXCERPT)

DENNIS
FOON

Characters

JOSH

CHARLA

PAIGE

ADAM

They are all in grade seven.

Puppets

All the other characters are played by animated objects, puppets, masked figures or voices. They include:

TV

MISHA, Paige's half-brother

MOM, Paige's mother

DAD, Paige's stepfather

ANNE, Josh's mother

BILL, Josh's father

ELLEN, Charla's mother

MICKY

ZEDNIK

NYTRO

CAT, Adam's mother

DOG, Adam's stepfather

Most of the puppets are described in the text; directors and casts are encouraged to explore creative ways of realizing these characters. The following notes describe some of the approaches taken by the original production.

I describe Josh's parents in the play as an "attaché case" and a "telephone." In the original production, we decided not to make these two characters puppets. The actors wore head pieces that allowed a clear view of their faces. BILL had a visor that he snapped down when he went into business mode and carried a cellular phone; ANNE had a spinning wheel that had her appointments clipped to it and carried an attaché case that contained a heart, a Nintendo game and Josh's lunch money.

MISHA was a two-foot-high doll with a spinning head that had two faces: one angelic, the other demonic, complete with pointed teeth and horns. Paige's parents only saw his angelic side. Paige, of course, was constantly exposed to the demon.

The actors playing ADAM, CHARLA, PAIGE and JOSH each carried a hand puppet that represented their "secret" or "inner" self. In moments of hurt, loneliness or fear they put on the hand puppet and comforted it.

The play may be performed by as few as four actors. However, the final scene with NYTRO may require an "assist" by the stage manager.

The Set

The play takes place in many different locations but the only stage-requirement is a large "brick" wall masking the upstage area.

Covered in graffiti, the wall is the place where Adam goes to draw his bird, the eagle that eventually emerges from behind the bricks.

This wall also provides Nytro a place to "crash" through and a position (at the top of the wall) for the operators to control the human Ellen in her last scene with Charla.

In the original production, four cubes were used to create all the different environments. For example, the *top of an overstuffed chair sat on one of the cubes to represent Adam's house. The back of the chair had the house's exterior painted on it and when this side faced the audience it represented the front porch of Adam's house. When the chair was turned around to face the audience, it represented the inside of Adam's house. Adam sat in the chair and the dog and cat fought on the overstuffed arms.*

Adam: Where're you goin', Josh?

Josh: In … inta school.

Adam: You didn't even say hi to me. Don't you say hello?

Josh: Hello.

Adam: (*Poking him.*) Hello, what?

Josh: Hello, Adam.

Adam: (*Shoving him.*) What did you call me?

Josh: Adam.

Adam: Did I say you could call me that?

Josh: No.

Adam: Then why'd you say it?

Josh: I don't know.

Adam: What?

Josh: I don't know.

Adam: What?

Josh: I don't know.

Adam: What?

Josh: I don't know.

(ADAM shoves JOSH several times, pushing him out of earshot of the girls.)

Adam: You wanna live?

Josh: Yes.

Adam: Then whattaya got for me today?

(JOSH reaches into his pocket, gives ADAM the two dollar bill.)

Is that all?

Josh: Uh-huh.

Adam: Are you holding out on me?

Josh: No.

(ADAM squeezes JOSH's face.)

Adam: You better not be, Wimpsucker.

(ADAM throws JOSH on the ground and struts away, smiling at the girls. PAIGE is not impressed. CHARLA runs over to JOSH.)

Charla: Are you okay?

(JOSH gets up. CHARLA hands him his school pack. JOSH takes it and runs off.)

Paige: I'm Paige. Are you new here?

Charla: First day. I'm Charla. What's with that Adam?

Paige: Oh, he does that to everybody but especially Josh. He steals too—did you see him try to kiss me?

Charla: Yeah.

Paige: He's not the only one. Kim tried to kiss me yesterday. He said he wants to be my boyfriend—I told him to

stick his head in the toilet. Roy was my boyfriend from February to May but I broke up with him 'cause he ate too much pizza.

Charla: Too much pizza?

Paige: The tomato sauce gave him a red moustache, it was gross—do you have a boyfriend?

Charla: No.

Paige: My boyfriend is Micky.

(MICKY enters. He is a trendily dressed, boy mannequin on wheels. An operator works his arms.)

He's the cutest boy in the whole school. He even did a TV commercial he's so cute. And met [Kirsty Alley] and gave me her autograph.

(MICKY goes to PAIGE and holds her hand.)

I love the presents he gives me.

(MICKY hands PAIGE some pencils and puts a ring on her finger.)

And he gave me his ring to wear. Don't you love it? I know some people who would kill for it. But he gave it to me ... I don't mind kissing Micky 'cause we're in love.

(PAIGE kisses MICKY. CHARLA is embarrassed. MICKY exits.)

Everybody says he's the most popular boy in school and I'm the most popular girl. Do you think that's true? Of course, you wouldn't know, you just got here.

Charla: I haven't even been to class yet.

Paige: We have a group, you know. Of really special people.

We go skating together and to the mall. Wanna be in it?

Charla: Sure.

Paige: Okay. I'll talk to everybody. I mean it's really my decision and everything but I have to keep it fair, you know what I mean?

Charla: Yeah.

Paige: So I'll let you know, okay?

Charla: Okay.

(As PAIGE exits, she waves to a friend.)

Paige: Hi!

(CHARLA watches her go.

The school bell rings. All four kids take their places for class. ADAM comes in last. Before he sits, he goes to JOSH and smacks him on the head.)

Adam: Get outta my seat.

Josh: The teacher put me here.

Adam: Well who's in charge, me or him?

Josh: … He's the teacher.

(ADAM smacks JOSH again.)

Adam: Who's your boss?

(JOSH moves to the next seat.)

Good very good. You get a star.

(ADAM snaps his finger at JOSH's face.

ADAM sits in a different seat, leaving JOSH's original place empty. ADAM takes out his piece of paper and draws on it.)

MR. ZEDNIK, unseen by the audience, enters the classroom. All four kids sit up straight.

They perform ZEDNIK's voice in unison. When speaking his voice, they look down at their desks; when speaking directly to ZEDNIK, they look up.)

Zednik: Good morning class.

All: Good morning Mr. Zednik.

Zednik: We have a new student in our class. I'd like you all to welcome Charla Williams. Josh?

Josh: Yes, sir?

Zednik: Why aren't you sitting in your correct seat?

Josh: I ...

Zednik: Well, move.

(JOSH quickly moves back into his original place.)

Now. Your book presentations. Who would like to go first?

(PAIGE eagerly holds up her hand.)

Alright, Paige.

Paige: My report is on the autobiography of [Claudia Schiffer]. From the moment she was born, everybody knew she was going to be a superstar because she was such a perfect baby and didn't cry at all.

(ADAM pokes JOSH with his pencil. JOSH moves over in his seat to get away.)

Did you know that [Claudia Schiffer's] hair grows faster than normal people's? Her hair was rated the most perfect by the Hairdressers Association of North America.

(ADAM pokes JOSH again with his pencil. JOSH moves away but this time falls off his chair.)

Zednik: Josh, are you okay?

Josh: Yes, sir.

Zednik: What happened?

Josh: I ... I slipped.

Zednik: Adam?

Adam: Yes, sir?

Zednik: Did you push Josh?

Adam: No, sir.

Zednik: Did you poke him?

Adam: With what, sir?

Zednik: You tell me.

Adam: No way I could reach him from my seat, sir. Besides, all I got is my eraser in my hand and that wouldn't poke him very well, do you think, sir?

Zednik: Alright then, get your notebooks out for a dictation exercise.

(As they pull out their notebooks, ADAM folds up the piece of paper he's been working on and passes it to CHARLA, indicating that she should give it to PAIGE. CHARLA does.)

What are you doing, Charla?

Charla: Getting out a notebook, sir.

Zednik: Very good, Charla. Pencils ready? The first sentence is: Blah blah blah blah blah blah.

(The bell rings. The kids run out.

JOSH sits by himself. CHARLA starts to go to him but is stopped by PAIGE.)

Paige: How'd you like my book report?

Charla: It was interesting.

Paige: I should hope so, I made it all up.

Charla: You did?

Paige: Yeah! I didn't have to read a book. I heard something about her hair on TV. And that stuff about the baby? That's what they said about me, when I was born. Perfect baby. Didn't cry. Superstar. What'd they say about you?

Charla: I don't remember.

(PAIGE reaches into her pocket.)

Paige: Oh, right, Adam's note.

(She opens it.)

What is this?

Charla: It's a drawing.

Paige: It's weird.

Charla: It's nice.

Paige: You're weird. What does it say?

Charla: It's crossed out. It says—I … love you.

Paige: Lemmee see that. *(She giggles.)* What a goof.

(She throws it on the ground.)

Charla: Don't you want it?

Paige: Are you kidding? It's got germs. Did you see the new [Vogue]?

Charla: No.

(PAIGE pulls it out, points at the cover.)

Paige: I love that colour on her.

Charla: It would look good on you too.

Paige: You think so?

Charla: That shade of blue's perfect for you.

Paige: Maybe if I grew my hair.

Charla: I was thinking about growing mine too.

Paige: I'm gonna perm mine like hers.

Charla: That'd look great.

Paige: You should perm yours too.

(MICKY enters.)

Micky!

(MICKY holds up his wrist. He is wearing a watch.)

What's that? A Rolex! (*To CHARLA.*) His uncle gave him a real Rolex for his birthday! (*To MICKY.*) Is that your uncle who lives in Hollywood? The one who helped produce [Terminator Two]?

(MICKY pulls out his date book.)

A birthday party? I think it'd be great at your house. Musicman for DJ? Perfect, he's the best. Printed invitations? Good idea.

(She starts making a list.)

Who should we invite? Boys: Sean, Jason, Justin, Ben, Chris, Alex …

(She looks at JOSH, who's immersed in a Gameboy. She

facetiously motions to MICKY, as if to say, "Should we invite him?" She giggles, then back to her list.)

Brent, Chad, Jake. Girls: Catherine, Julia, Tuesday …

(CHARLA watches PAIGE hopefully.)

Michelle, Melissa, Emily, Sara, Rebecca …

(MICKY makes a point.)

No, Micky, not Allison M, she's boring. Stephanie, Kristen, Kimberly …

(PAIGE looks at CHARLA as she tries to think of the last name. CHARLA is on the edge of her seat hoping.)

Monica! I think that's everybody. Okay, let's go … see you later, Charla.

Charla: Bye.

(CHARLA sadly watches PAIGE and MICKY go. PAIGE turns, calling back to CHARLA.)

Paige: Call me!

Charla: What's your number?

Activities

1. Create a character web for each of the four main characters — Josh, Adam, Charla, and Paige. Show physical characteristics, key personality traits, and other background information about the characters.

2. Work with a partner. For a production of this play excerpt, decide on appropriate costumes and props for Micky and each of the four main characters. Write descriptions of these costumes and props.

3. Work with a group of six actors and a director. Rehearse and present this play excerpt to the class.

Tricks of the Trade

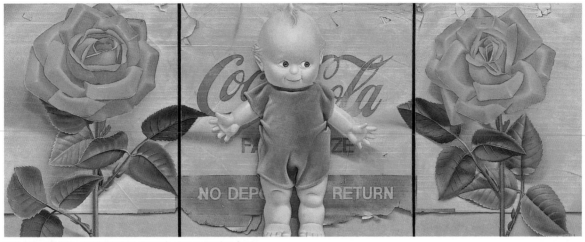

Doll John Hall, 1971, National Gallery of Canada, Ottawa. Purchased 1972.

Advertising jingles, slogans, scripts, and descriptions—called *advertising copy* in the ad world—have power, sometimes more power than you might like. They enter your head uninvited and make themselves at home, while you struggle to remember the names of the world's longest rivers or a friend's telephone number. If you watch ten minutes of TV commercials and spend an hour studying French, why is it easier to remember the advertising jingles than the French vocabulary?

Ad copy writers grab our attention with the same tricks that poets have always relied upon. Rhyme. Rhythm. Repetition. Surprises. Puns. Humour. They break grammatical rules, they make up words. And they make us believe they're having fun doing it.

"Whose news do most choose?" asks *Maclean's* magazine. "The Bread Spread," chant the mayonnaise people. "Dirty … Dingy … Dazzling," proclaim the makers of

Tide. "Very Lush, Very Lavish, Very Factor," boasts a cosmetics company, counting on name recognition. Revlon's writers get funny with "Drop Dead Nails" and "Lash chance for sensitive eyes." "A Clearly Grate Italian," puns the ad for TreStelle Parmesan cheese. "Wild Thin … a ferocious flavour experience," promises Diet Orange Crush.

Ad copy writers use words that are juicy and slurpy. Words you can taste and hear. Some words, when spoken, sound like their meanings. They are called *onomatopoetic* words. Try this list on your ear: *Boom, burst, buzz, chortle, click, crash, fizz, grizzle, growl, hiss, luminous, muck, poof, pop, rock, scratch, shriek, smack, spurt, zip.*

Advertisers rely on repetition. Not only do commercials appear over and over on the radio and TV and in print media, but there is also repetition within ads. Like poets, advertisers repeat particular sounds, groups of sounds, and rhythmic patterns of sound to attract attention and make a lasting impression. One common "trick of the trade" is rhyme. Rhyming sounds usually appear at the ends of words or groups of words: Swiss Miss, Ace is the place, Big Mac Attack. However, both poets and advertisers also use alliteration, as in Peter Pan Peanut Butter, Relaxed Riders, and even throughout words like Coca-Cola, making the brand names easy to remember.

Another classic device of both ad writers and poets is the simile, a comparison using the words *like* or *as*. "It's like opening a present," promises a Polaroid Colour Pack Camera ad, showing a picture of a boy with a half-eaten stick of ice cream. Similes make you see things in a new way.

Ad copy writers know that some words sell products and others don't. They know that *half-full* sounds better than *half-empty,* and that an *engine* sounds more complicated and expensive than a *motor.* *Thin* is a nicer word than *skinny,* and *artificial* sounds bad for us, but *man-made* sounds good. They know their way around the mysterious world of word-choice, or word-feel, where for no very logical reason certain words make us feel stingy or cheap, while other words make us feel flush and fine and ready to part with our hard-earned money. Ad copy writers say that even particular syllables convey feelings. For example, they suggest that words containing the syllable "eep" convey low or mean feelings, words containing "eal" are weak and unhealthy, and words with "urk" are evil, grotesque, or abnormal.

But are ad writers really poets? Aren't they just selling a product or a company? Laundry detergent, jeans, hair spray, or sneakers—it's all the same to them. True poets have something more serious to say. Right?

Well, that's partly right. But the best ad writers know that they are selling more than a product. They're aware that aside from variations in packaging, most products are surprisingly similar. There's not much difference among fluoride toothpastes, or between one dog biscuit and another. If you took the labels off all the jeans in a clothing store, could you tell the brands apart? Ad writers must distinguish their product in some way to set it off from the pack. So, like poets, they try to sell us a mood or a sunset, a feeling or a point of view. They must wake us up, surprise us, shock us, or give us a happy ending.

An ad must persuade you that it's not just dog biscuits in that box. It's your dog's love and affection. It's not just a pair of jeans attached to that label. It's romance, glamour, popularity. The right toothpaste will brighten not just teeth but your whole morning, help solve family arguments, and give you the courage to invite some special person to the high school dance.

Advertising is a big, expensive business. Because the success of a product often rides on the words an advertising copy writer strings together, every word must sell. In 1992, Canada spent more than ten billion dollars on advertising, almost all of it to pay for media space. With that much money on the line, no advertising copy can afford to laze around. Every word must literally be worth its weight in gold.

Activities

1. Prepare a mini-lesson for the class on one of the following literary techniques or elements: rhyme, rhythm, repetition, onomatopoeia, simile, euphemism, metaphor. Present your mini-lesson to the class, using an overhead that includes the term, a definition of it in your own words, and examples of it from the article. Take notes on each other's presentations, evaluating them for clarity of speech and visuals and for accuracy of information.

2. Find specific advertisements that include examples of the techniques and elements described in the article. For class display, create a collage of the examples you've found.

3. Work with a partner. Consider the statement in the article that "every word must be worth its weight in gold" in advertising. What exactly does this mean? Would you make the same statement about poetry? Develop another metaphor to describe poems and explain your metaphor to the class.

Barbie Collectibles

MATTEL, INC.

*I*nside every woman is an adult and a child.

The child in you will dream of bright summer days in the park. Of elegant ladies in stylish turn-of-the-century walking suits. Of parasols and feathered hats. The adult in you will admire her authenticity, craftsmanship and timeless quality. Promenade In The Park Barbie® doll is made specially for the collector and filled with charming details. From her extravagant earrings to her elegant

They should

get to know

each other better.

necklace, she is a symbol of a bygone era, marked by poise and grace. Call now for a free catalog or store locations at 1-888-777-0010 (U.S./Canada). Available for around $60 ($85 in Canada).

Barbie
COLLECTIBLES
www.barbie.com

Activities

1. Who is the target audience for this advertisement? What needs are the manufacturers appealing to? List evidence to support your view.

2. Work with a small group. For each of the following people, brainstorm a list of the thoughts and feelings you think that person might have about the advertisement: a doll collector, a feminist writer, a seven-year-old girl, a career woman, a mother, a father. Present the different points of view to the class.

Messages Are

against animal testing

The language of advertising is important. How does "Not Tested on Animals" differ from "Against Animal Testing"? Does this T-shirt make fun of the real issue?

Where an ad is placed can be as important as what it contains. Who would choose to advertise on a school bus? Should schools allow advertisers to promote products on school property?

YOU DID IT!   NICE TRY!   REALLY IMPROVED!   WOW!   GOOD EFFORT!   DOING WELL!

Everywhere!

Why do so many personal-care products have the phrase "Not tested on animals" featured prominently on their labels? And why would a hair-products company donate money for breast cancer research?

Miso Soup Dashi (BONITO FLAKES) (JAPANESE STOCK)

3 cups (750 ml)   water
½ cup (25 grams)   bonito flakes (fish flakes)

Bring water to a boil and add flakes. Remove from heat and let stand until flakes settle, about 5 minutes. Remove any foam, strain.

One way we learn about cultures different from ours is through their food. How do you feel about trying a food you've never eaten before? In your community, how much food from other cultures is available?

EXCELLENT!

GOOD

THINKING!

AWESOME!

What are these stickers conveying? How might they be used, and what effect might their use have?

Handling **ANGER** and Resolving **CONFLICT**

At Twelve Sally Mann

Focus Your Learning

Reading this article will help you to:

- summarize information
- make appropriate use of different formats to suit content, audience, and purpose
- plan and facilitate a group role-playing activity
- evaluate your own and your group's work and set goals for improvement

It's clear that different things provoke, or stir up, anger in different people. For example, last Friday night Erica, Aaron, Daryl, and Tamika went to their favourite pizza place. They had to wait a long time to be seated. Aaron, Daryl, and Tamika were so busy talking that they didn't notice the wait. Erica, however, got angrier and angrier. "They always serve adults first," she muttered. She folded her arms across her chest and glared at the waiters.

After the group was finally seated, Erica slowly relaxed and joined in on the conversation. Then a baby at the next table began crying. Erica, Aaron, and Tamika didn't seem to hear him, but Daryl rolled his eyes with each screech. "If that kid screams one more time …," he said through clenched teeth.

Daryl had spent too many hours listening to his baby sister cry at home. He surely didn't need to hear a baby screaming when he was out with his friends. He was angry because he thought the whole thing was unfair. Erica was angry because she thought the waiters didn't respect young people. Aaron and Tamika, on the other hand, were having fun—until it was time to go home.

On the way out of the crowded restaurant, Aaron bumped into a teenager he didn't know. The other boy called Aaron a name based on a group he thought Aaron belonged to. Aaron scowled all the way home, even though Daryl told him to forget about it. "He probably can't even spell that word," Daryl joked.

Just as we have different skin colours and different goals, we feel angry over different things. Whether we become angry in a certain situation depends on many things. These things include our past experiences, our values, our self-confidence, and what we tell ourselves about the situation.

For example, if you tease me about my new haircut, I will smile. I know you are teasing me because you like me. If a stranger says the same thing, however, I may think he or she is putting me down. My reaction will be different, probably anger.

Anger is a normal emotion that occurs often during conflicts. What we do with our anger can either solve the conflict or turn it into a lasting problem.

Understanding the Causes of Anger

Stress is one major cause of anger. Stress is the pressure we feel in certain situations. Adrian is feeling stressed because she has an important report to finish tonight and a job to go to after school. As she hurries toward her locker after school, her friend Kelly stops her.

"Things are bad at home," Kelly says. "Do you have time to talk tonight?" What happens next surprises even Adrian. She snaps, "Can't you handle it yourself this time?" Adrian's stress has resulted in a kind of free-floating anger.

Frustration is similar to stress. We feel frustration when we can't reach goals that are important to us. Juan, for example, is determined to make the varsity football team this year. He's been eating right, working out with weights, and going to every practice. Now Coach Reynolds is posting the varsity team list on the bulletin board. The coach avoids looking at Juan. Juan knows then that his name isn't on the list.

Juan mutters, "Maybe the team wouldn't have such a lousy record if you picked some good players for a change!" The coach hears him and frowns. Juan's frustration has become anger. He has made a disappointing situation even worse.

Feeling *threatened* can also lead to anger, especially when the threat is to our self-esteem. Almost anything can be seen as a threat: a look, a shove, a putdown, a turned back, a phone call that isn't returned, not being waited on in a store. Any of these can communicate disrespect (or we may think they do). If we think others do not respect us, we often have angry feelings.

Being treated like a stereotype is another form of disrespect. Do you ever hear comments like the following ones? Whether the disrespect is intended or not, our anger level rises.

- "The music you kids listen to is disgusting."
- "Students with your background don't do well in college."
- "Girls aren't good at math."

Still, no one has to be at the mercy of anger. We can learn ways to control anger and make it work for us, not against us.

Personal Peeves

Jarod is walking past a group of students. Some of them are his friends. As he walks past the group, they start laughing.

Are they laughing at me? They better not be, but why would they? Chip over there is on the soccer team with me. He's my friend. Wait—maybe he told them what happened at practice yesterday. No, he wouldn't do that. At least, I don't think he would.

But why are they laughing? Angelo is in my English class, and I had to give my report this morning. So I dropped all my note cards, but it wasn't that funny.

Maybe it's some kind of practical joke these kids pull on people who walk past them, just to see how they take it. I'm tough, but I don't like this at all.

Jarod is feeling pretty uncomfortable right now. He has a lot of mixed messages running through his head, most of them making him angry. He might be surprised to know that these young people are laughing at a joke one of the girls just told. No one in the group probably even noticed him.

How Not to Handle Conflict

No matter what kind of conflict we face, certain approaches work better than others. Just as each person develops a way of communicating, each person also develops a way of handling conflict. Our way of communicating greatly influences how we handle conflict.

During a conflict, Passive Paul keeps his eyes on the floor. He doesn't try to explain his point of view or his feelings. Instead, he may apologize for whatever happened, even if he did nothing wrong. He is so uncomfortable that he doesn't use his listening skills to try to find out how the other person feels. He just stands there with his head down, ready to escape as soon as he can.

Aggressive Andy doesn't listen either. He doesn't care what anyone else thinks. Andy matches his loud demands with angry gestures. His gestures are designed to discourage others from voicing their opinions. Andy interrupts others whenever he feels like it.

NO ONE HAS TO BE AT THE MERCY OF ANGER

Positive Problem-Solving

KC has lost Ashley's sunglasses and can't afford to replace them. Assertive Ashley uses straightforward, learnable skills to resolve this conflict and save her friendship with KC. Here are the steps that she takes:

1. *Get Ready*

First, Ashley does her best to forget any past disagreements with KC and to focus on today's problem. She takes a few deep breaths to clear away any angry feelings. Then she asks herself if she is ready to handle this. If she were still too angry, she would tell KC that she wants to talk about the sunglasses later, when she is calmer.

2. *Listen*

Ashley listens carefully to KC's side of the conflict and asks questions. She repeats what she thinks KC said in order to see if she really understands KC's point of view.

3. *Explain*

Then Ashley uses an "I message" to explain her needs: "I feel angry that you lost my sunglasses because I need them for the baseball game tomorrow." As she speaks, Ashley stands tall and confident, looking KC in the eye. She doesn't blame KC for being careless, and she doesn't act disgusted.

Activities

1. Work with a small group. Brainstorm situations where you might use the skills identified in the article. Develop a role play around one or two of these situations, using criteria for effective role plays developed by the class. Present your role play to the class. Complete a self-evaluation of your participation in the group project and set goals for improvement.

2. Imagine that you are an Anger Management Counsellor who must present the information in this article to a class of younger students. Summarize and restructure the information into visual formats such as cause-and-effect and other charts so that the students will clearly understand the causes of anger. Present your work to a local elementary school class for feedback on its clarity and effectiveness.

3. Rework your presentation so that it is appropriate for an audience of teachers.

The Child Who Walks Backwards

Lake Simcoe Garden J. E. H. MacDonald

Lorna Crozier

My next-door neighbour tells me
her child runs into things.
Cupboard corners and doorknobs
have pounded their shapes
into his face. She says
he is bothered by dreams,
rises in sleep from his bed
to steal through the halls
and plummet like a wounded bird
down the flight of stairs.

This child who climbed my maple

with the sureness of a cat,

trips in his room, cracks

his skull on the bedpost,

smacks his cheeks on the floor.

When I ask about the burns

on the back of his knee,

his mother tells me

he walks backwards

into fireplace grates

or sits and stares at flames

while sparks burn stars in his skin.

Other children write their names

on the casts that hold

his small bones.

His mother tells me

he runs into things,

walks backwards,

breaks his leg

while she lies

sleeping.

Life Sentence

NICOLE AXWORTHY

Detail from **The Sick Girl** Edvard Munch

She exists in my mind and she nags me, "Why are you eating this? You'll get fat. You're just ugly and fat and you can't do anything right!" I don't know why she makes me cry. She's like the bully that takes your money at lunch, but she never goes away. She sleeps with me at night. She greets me in the shower every morning. She scorns me at every meal. I call her the Beast. I never get a moment's peace. I want to grab her and throw her down but I can't. She controls me. She goes deep into my mind and body where all is cold and dark and empty.

I never planned to disappear, at least not totally. My goal was a modest one: to be perfect. Unfortunately, something went wrong. I even remember the moment I became conscious of this, this mission you could call it, this extreme change in my life. Spring, Grade Eight: I was walking home from volleyball practice one depressingly rainy day. I was overwhelmed by raindrops, and the thick fog that clouded my view. The lightness of the air expanded like helium in my head. My brain became a radiant blur, my limbs very long and light, and I tried with slow motion steps to negotiate the oddly slanting sidewalk. I tried to focus. I only remembered what was to come when I got home: dinner. Another meal, another lie, another fight with my parents.

But that day I found a way to keep myself going. Concentrate. Focus on this

rule: the worse you feel, the better you are, the emptier, the freer, the purer. Know how it feels to be human, when all insulation has been stripped away. Think of all the people on this planet who have no choice.

"The worse you feel, the better you are," I repeated, chanting it inside my head, timing my steps to its insistent beat. That kept me going for quite a while. It gave me the courage to fight against all others in order to keep control. I had control of my life. Eventually, I didn't need those encouraging words any longer. I had reached such a pitch of discipline that my every thought was beyond my control.

I couldn't imagine forcing once-favourite foods down my esophagus. It fascinated yet disgusted me to catch someone in the act. In the food court of the mall, I found myself staring, appalled at a fat woman cramming a hamburger into her mouth. And then chewing. She glanced at me with a look of guilt, and I nervously looked down to measure the smallness of my wrist with my thumb and forefinger. Watching her was the lewdest sight I could imagine. How could anyone do something so indecent in public, especially someone who shouldn't be eating at all? I stared and stared, deafened by the Beast inside my head. Later I realized I was still staring, forgetting to blink, though she had long since left. Such things happened many times: missing a reel of the movie, or seeing, for a spell, only the black space between frames.

I thought I was functioning perfectly well. I didn't waste time eating and sleeping and chasing after sex like everyone else my age. I just worked at school, obsessed over every calorie I took in, and cried all the time. I felt like a "star" in the Diet Department because I had so much willpower, and I could control my eating habits more than anyone I knew. Nothing else seemed happy or exciting to me in the six months or so before I went to the hospital. I remember almost nothing else from those long, mute, vitiated days.

It's 5:00 a.m. and I should be stretching for my run, but how am I going to run here,

when they won't even let me walk farther than the bathroom? I could run in place for 45 minutes, but what about this stupid heart monitor? I would have to turn it off for now. It's a good thing I was watching when the nurse did it yesterday. So, by my calculations, I have an hour and a half before Nursey bursts in.

Sure enough, at precisely 6:30 there's a knock at the door, which opens almost immediately, giving me just enough time to leap back on the bed and stick the monitor leads on my chest. I try to look as if I'm lying there contemplating the ceiling, but I feel flushed and a little out of breath from running. At least I never sweat any more.

"Good morning," she chirps, glancing at the heart monitor and then eyeing me suspiciously. "How did you sleep?"

"Fine," I lie.

"Have you been awake for long?" she asks. "If you wake up early, or you can't sleep, you can always ring for the night nurse."

"No, I'm fine, thanks."

"Well, here's your breakfast," she says, as if I haven't already figured out what is on the huge tray. "We're going to weigh you afterward and decide what needs to be done, so see how much of it you can eat, okay?"

What needs to be done is for everybody to just leave me alone, to let me eat my own food in my own way. Here, every meal is going to be a struggle, I can see, looking over the enormous load.

I'm confronted with a huge mound of corn flakes heaping over the rim of the bowl (about 200 calories); a large container of 2% milk (256 calories); half a grapefruit (35 calories); two pieces of whole wheat toast (180 calories), dry I'm glad to see, though there are four pats of butter (110 calories); a boiled egg (79 calories), and a cup of tea.

I decide I will eat the grapefruit half and one piece of toast. That ought to make them happy. For a moment I think of throwing the cereal away to make it look as if I've eaten that too but I can't think of a place to hide it.

Slowly, delicately, precisely, I cut the piece of toast into halves, then quarters, then eighths, and daintily convey each piece to my mouth, allowing three minutes between bites. Then, in the same way, I eat the grapefruit, panicking for a moment. How can anything so heart-rendingly sweet have so few calories? What if they've sprinkled sugar all over it, so I can't see it? What if this is some special high-calorie grapefruit, grown especially for hospitals? Something is definitely wrong because this vivid sweetness is lingering on my taste buds, tempting me to eat more.

But I don't. When I've finished the grapefruit, my heart is hammering: I put the tray on the other bed, as far away from me as possible. The tray still looks loaded, despite everything I've consumed.

Time for the big weigh-in and I'm afraid: afraid that I have gained weight under this regime of force-feeding; afraid that I won't have gained and will have to stay here forever having huge trays of food pushed at me, maybe even having tubes rammed in me. The nurse is chattering away mindlessly as she wheels me to the examining room: "It's a beautiful day outside," she says. "Take off your socks and step on the scale."

The beam doesn't move at first, and then she slides the weight along and it lifts, quivering gently. With a shock I see that the metal tooth has snagged just about 69. Sixty-nine and one-half pounds! I've gained a whole pound in three days and only half of that is the five glasses of water I drank before being wheeled here. My stomach feels close to bursting and suddenly looks obscenely round. As panic surges, I try to remind myself why I am here. I'm here to become healthy again. Oh, how I loathe that word. I'm here because my father couldn't take it any more and told my doctor, "She needs to go in the hospital. I'm afraid she's going to die."

Hospital, school, prison: it's becoming increasingly difficult to tell the difference. And here at least I'm no bother to my family. I know now that I was the whole time I was home. The fights, the screaming matches, the throwing of food across the room was just too much.

Some kind of sadness comes over me, so I turn off the TV and go back to my room. I lie down on my bed, where I've spent so much time, where so much of my life has been eaten away, and I close my eyes, covering my face with my arms. The usual thoughts start to arrive—ugly, mushy, fatty flesh. I try to think about something else. I think about something happy, something sun-kissed. Then, I can't help it, I think of the guilt, the fear, the hatred. I am a wasted body, a wasted life.

This is the body I must learn to inhabit; or to coinhabit, rather. It feels like an alien has fastened to my body, reprogramming my DNA to produce itself instead of me. I don't know if I can. That spare, vacant frame gave me so much space to hide in.

Can I learn to be so present?

Can I learn to be so full?

Activities

1. As you read this article, jot down phrases or images that appeal to your emotions. Summarize Nicole's struggle by creating a poem with these phrases and images.

2. Imagine that you are Nicole's parents. Write a letter to her explaining why you put her in hospital. Trade letters with a classmate and respond to his or her letter as if you were Nicole.

3. Work with a partner. Research facts and statistics about eating disorders. Use this information to create a pamphlet for distribution to a teenage audience. If possible, use a word-processing program to help you design and lay out your pamphlet.

Making Canadian *Hockey* History

Locker-Room Talk with Today's Famous Five

ROBIN WHEELER

Focus Your Learning
Reading this article will help you to:
- plan and facilitate a small-group activity involving role play
- rethink in the light of new information
- develop and evaluate a poster

I met five of the members of Team Canada in the "cool-down" room at *Canadian Hockey*, fresh out of cardio training. Here they train for the 1998 Winter Olympics in Nagano, Japan. Here, for this year, these women make playing hockey a career for the first time ever.

The women sip Gatorade and munch granola bars as the interview begins. Time is short. The next bout of training will begin for most of them as soon as our conversation ends.

In Nagano, women's hockey will have its first official Olympic showing. The pressure to perform is intense for Team Canada. They beat the pressure with banter. The jokes fly between them as quickly as the puck.

The jokes suggest a level of comfort, of easygoing friendship, which is one of the team's strengths, and which comes from working hard together toward a common goal: Gold. They can lean on one another. If no one else is handy, they joke, there is always Princess, a plastic toy who has been everywhere they have.

These are women. Not men. Playing Canada's sport. A sport we've come to associate with men, with hard-hitting play, with spit and grit and physical strength. These are women. But make no mistake: they've come this far because they're strong. They've passed the lactate test. They grew up beating the boys at hockey, and they don't expect to be challenged at this stage for something as stupid as gender. It doesn't matter if it's the men's team or the women's. They're Team Canada, and they're tough: tough physically, tough mentally, and—yes—as a team, tough to beat.

That said, the tape rolls, the women finish their drinks, and for the rest of this conversation, they speak for themselves.

The Game

Is women's hockey as hard-hitting as men's?
Diduck jokes: We hit more!
Stacy: There's no intentional bodychecking, but it's a very physical game.

What differences exist between the women's game and the men's technically?
Wick: There are a lot of differences, but mainly it's the size and speed. In the women's game you get a lot of shots from closer into the net whereas with the men's game the shot tends to come from the outside because they're bigger and stronger and the play develops earlier.

What's the reality of being a woman playing a "man's" game?
Stacy: I think all sports started with mostly males playing or mostly females playing. But they evolve and both genders are now involved with most sports ... It's a game and both genders can play it. There might

be some differences between us, whether it's the moves or just the fact that size and strength are different, but all this gender stuff, I don't think it has a place in sport.

Diduck: And I think it's the tradition too. Hockey is traditionally a men's game and you can't overlook that. People see women's hockey and it's new and they're skeptical at first and that's only natural.

Have you received criticism from men or other women for playing hockey?

Becca: I haven't really had any bad experiences. Wick on the other hand …

Wick: I've seen a lot of things, but now it's come to the point where you're not criticized as much. When you're younger it's mostly the parents who tend to say things … Parents just don't get it. They want their kids going to the NHL and that's just a fact. It's pressure. There's a lot of pressure on younger boys I think.

Can you give an example?

Wick: I could give you lots but … A mad parent actually came to the dressing room when I was changing and went on and on … "Don't hit my son," that was basically the point. But it was just basically negative comments.

Diduck: I don't think it happens much any more. Once you show them that you can pass and shoot and skate it tends to go away.

Jen: It's like everything in life. You get two different perspectives on things. A lot of people are just really impressed with the calibre of your playing, and I guess there's always the other side of things where people can be pessimists and look down on things.

As kids, did girls stand out playing a "boy's" game?

Diduck: They stood out, but I think the guys wouldn't really accept you unless you were adequate at athletics. Most of the time the girls were better than the guys. So there was a natural acceptance. They had to accept you because you were better than them.

Jen: They wouldn't let you play if you weren't good.

Becca: And you wouldn't want to be there … you had to fit in or you wouldn't be having fun anyway.

How has hockey changed for women since you started?

Jen: It's changing so fast. There are more leagues for girls at a younger age. When we were that age, it hadn't grown that much. There weren't leagues for us to play in.

Now it's changing every day. I think there will be more girls playing than ever before.

But when you guys were kids were you more often playing with the boys?
Wick: Always.

Who is Princess?
Diduck: Princess is a plastic McDonald's toy. She's been everywhere. She's ridden in planes, done the lactate test.
Stacy: She's pretty much an honorary member of Team Canada.
Diduck: Honorary—she's worked hard.

Tell me about the lactate test.
Diduck: You skate down and back and down and back …
Becca: … four-and-a-half lengths and then you stop for two minutes and then you do five reps. On your fifth you go and get your finger pricked. They draw blood and run tests to determine how high your lactate level is …
Wick: The more lactate you have the harder you can work.
Stacy: At the end of it though, your legs won't move and you pretty much can't feel them.
Becca: You get past the point of pain.

The Gap

I'm interested in that gap. (The team laughs.)
Becca: "Control the gap"—it's a term in hockey.

What differences exist between the older and younger members of the team? Stacy, you've been a teacher for nine years. Diduck, you run an entrepreneurial business. How has your experience been different from the younger women's?
Stacy: It's easy for them (referring to the team's younger members).
Diduck: They're coming into it and it's all kind of easy sailing for them … They're having every opportunity laid out in front of them right off the bat.

So for the younger players it was all there but for you guys …?
Stacy: It's a different experience for everybody concerned, but being that we're, on average, probably ten years older, there's a big gap there. It's like Hayley saying she played Canada Games when she was growing up. But Diduck and I …
Diduck: You were coaching Canada Games.
Stacy: Yes, I coached Canada Games

hockey. So it's just different opportunities, but I think they now have something to shoot for at a much younger age.

Do you younger players look up to the veterans?
Wick: You look up to them and they're role models for you because they brought the sport to where it is today. I think it makes for a good mix on the team too because we have people from all different walks of life and there's always somebody that can help with whatever situation you might be in.

How are relationships affected by hockey? Do you think about having families of your own?
Jen: I would like to, probably, but not for a long time.
Diduck: You can't. I shouldn't say you can't, but because hockey's always a priority it's pretty unlikely that you'd have a family …
Stacy: … We work all day, we train at night, and on the weekends we play hockey. That doesn't leave much time for anything else.
Diduck: … When you're little you have your plan, you know: I'd be married at twenty-one, at twenty-five I'd start having kids … However, it's now many years later. But I don't think it's unusual in these times that you're married later, having kids later. People are just enjoying their youth and doing everything they possibly can.
Diduck: … You know guys, it's an interesting question: I wonder if, because we play sports, it's something we just don't feel we need?

Like you're already working outside the mould?
Diduck: Yes. I think some women get caught in that trap. I like men and I want them in my life, but if they're not there on a given week it's not like you can't survive without them.
Stacy: There are so many things out there to do, so many opportunities. Relationships? When they come along it's great but if they don't it's not a big deal.
Diduck: But I think with training for sport, it gives you a greater level of independence, self-confidence …
Stacy: In all sports, over the years you gain a sense of yourself and a sense that you're okay.

The Olympics

What pressures are associated with this experienced Team Canada, on the eve of its first official Olympic appearance?
Wick: I think there's the expectation that you should win a gold medal. You hear it from everybody.

You guys are the team to beat, right?
Diduck: Because we're from Canada. Hockey and Canada go together.
Stacy: I think you can put as much pressure on yourself as you want to. At the World Championships there were expectations—like the word Hayley used—there were expectations on us to be good. Whether to

take it as pressure is up to us. But the expectations are certainly there.

Is it easier being in a team sport?
Jen: It's easier.
Wick: Because you have support around you all the time. We support each other.
Diduck: And Princess listens really well too.
Stacy: This team has always been a close group. I think that's one of the best strengths it has …
Becca: Everybody's going through the same things. We all help each other. We go through different things at different times but I think everybody can relate.

Which team will be your greatest competition at Nagano?
Becca: The Americans and the Finns.

Stacy: China and Sweden are tough teams to play against too, very disciplined and demanding. It's a much more physical game.

How?
Becca: There's more stick work …
Diduck: It's hack and whack.
Becca: Over the years the gap between the higher-level countries and the lower-level countries has certainly tightened. You can't take anybody for granted.

Are you going to win?
Becca: Yes.
Stacy: That's the goal.
Jen: We want it. We all want to win at the Olympics. It helps us work hard.
Diduck: That's why we're here.

Activities

1. Work with a group of six. Brainstorm a list of common perceptions about hockey players. Assign each group member one of the roles in the article — the interviewer, Diduck, Stacy, Becca, Wick, Jen — and read the article aloud in role, videotaping the reading if possible for playback. As a group, discuss how your preconceived ideas about hockey players might have been challenged as you read the article. Still in role, write a list of advice that you would give a young woman who wanted to play higher-level hockey.

2. Work with a partner. Create a poster to encourage young girls to join hockey at an early age. Use criteria for effective advertisements developed by the class to create your poster and to evaluate it when it is completed.

Who Is Disabled?

Tony Wong

Author Tony Wong, a Jamaican, became paraplegic following an accident in 1978. He has been active ever since internationally on behalf of disabled people.

If you fail to see

the person

but only the disability,

then, who is blind?

If you cannot hear

your brother's

cry for justice,

who is deaf?

If you do not communicate with

your sister

but separate her from you,

who is disabled?

If your heart and your mind

do not reach out to

your neighbour,

who has the mental handicap?

If you do not stand up

for the rights of all

persons,

who is the cripple?

Your attitude towards

persons

with disabilities

may be our biggest handicap,

And yours too.

Activities

1. In your own words, write a paragraph explaining how the author builds the argument that the senses can fail to help us see past disabilities. Also summarize the advice the author gives to help us overcome our pre-judgements.

2. Write a poem which outlines how people might see you in a first impression, failing to see the "real" you. Consider using the senses to tie the poem together.

Day of the Butterfly

ALICE MUNRO

Transformations II Jack Shadbolt

I do not remember when Myra Sayla came to town, though she must have been in our

class at school for two or three years. I start remembering her in the last year, when her little brother Jimmy Sayla was in Grade One. Jimmy Sayla was not used to going to the bathroom by himself and he would have to come to the Grade Six door and ask for Myra and she would take him downstairs. Quite often he would not get to Myra in time and there would be a big dark stain on his little button-on cotton pants. Then Myra had to come and ask the teacher: "Please may I take my brother home, he has wet himself?"

That was what she said the first time and everybody in the front seats heard her—though Myra's voice was the lightest singsong—and there was a muted giggling which alerted the rest of the class. Our teacher, a cold, gentle girl who wore glasses with thin gold rims and in the stiff solicitude of certain poses resembled a giraffe, wrote something on a piece of paper and showed it to Myra. And Myra recited uncertainly, "My brother has had an accident, please, teacher."

Everybody knew of Jimmy Sayla's shame and at recess (if he was not being kept in, as he often was, for doing something he shouldn't in school) he did not dare go out on the school grounds, where the other little boys, and some bigger ones, were waiting to chase him and corner him against the back fence and thrash him with tree branches. He had to stay with Myra. But at our school there were the two sides, the Boys' Side and the Girls' Side, and it was believed that if you so much as stepped on the side that was not your own you might easily get the strap. Jimmy could not go out on the Girls' Side and Myra could not go out on the Boy's Side, and no one was allowed to stay in the school unless it was raining or snowing. So Myra and Jimmy spent every recess standing in the little back porch between the two sides. Perhaps they watched the baseball games, the tag and skipping and building of leaf houses in the fall and snow forts in the winter; perhaps they did not watch at all. Whenever you happened to look at them their heads were slightly bent, their narrow bodies hunched in, quite still. They had long smooth oval faces, melancholy and discreet—dark, oily, shining hair. The little boy's was long, clipped at home, and Myra's was worn in heavy braids coiled on top of her head so that she looked, from a distance, as if she was wearing a turban too big for her. Over their dark eyes the lids were never fully raised; they had a weary look. But it was more than that. They were like children in a medieval painting, they were like small figures carved of wood, for worship or magic, with faces smooth and aged, and meekly, cryptically uncommunicative.

Most of the teachers at our school had been teaching for a long time and at recess they would disappear into the teachers' room and not bother us. But our own teacher, the young woman of the fragile gold-rimmed glasses, was apt to watch us from a window and sometimes come out, looking brisk and uncomfortable, to stop a fight among the little girls or start a running game among the big ones, who had been huddled together playing Truth or Secrets. One day she came out and called, "Girls in Grade Six, I want to talk to you!" She smiled persuasively, earnestly, and with dreadful unease, showing fine gold rims around her teeth. She said, "There is a girl in Grade Six called Myra Sayla. She *is* in your grade, isn't she?"

We mumbled. But there was a coo from Gladys Healey. "Yes, Miss Darling!"

"Well, why is she never playing with the rest of you? Every day I see her standing in the back porch, never playing. Do you think she looks very happy standing back there? Do you think you would be very happy, if *you* were left back there?"

Nobody answered; we faced Miss Darling, all respectful, self-possessed, and bored with the unreality of her question. Then Gladys said, "Myra can't come out with us, Miss Darling. Myra has to look after her little brother!"

"Oh," said Miss Darling dubiously. "Well you ought to try to be nicer to her anyway. Don't you think so? Don't you? You will try to be nicer, won't you? I *know* you will." Poor Miss Darling! Her campaigns were soon confused, her persuasions turned to bleating and uncertain pleas.

When she had gone Gladys Healey said softly, "You will try to be nicer, won't you? I *know* you will!" and then drawing her lip back over her big teeth she yelled exuberantly, "I don't care if it rains or freezes."

She went through the whole verse and ended it with a spectacular twirl of her Royal Stuart tartan skirt. Mr. Healey ran a Dry Goods and Ladies' Wear, and his daughter's leadership in our class was partly due to her flashing plaid skirts and organdy blouses and velvet jackets with brass buttons, but also to her early-maturing bust and the fine brutal force of her personality. Now we all began to imitate Miss Darling.

We had not paid much attention to Myra before this. But now a game was developed; it started with saying, "Let's be nice to Myra!" Then we would walk up to her in formal groups of three or four and at a signal, say together, "Hel-lo Myra, Hello *My*-ra!" and follow up with something like, "What do you wash your hair in, Myra, it's so nice and shiny, *My*-ra." "Oh she washes it in cod-liver oil, don't you, Myra, she washes it in cod-liver oil, can't you smell it?"

And to tell the truth there was a smell about Myra, but it was a rotten-sweetish smell as of bad fruit. That was what the Saylas did, kept a little fruit store. Her father sat all day on a stool by the window, with his shirt open over his swelling stomach and tufts of black hair showing around his belly button; he chewed garlic. But if you went into the store it was Mrs. Sayla who came to wait on you, appearing silently between the limp print curtains hung across the back of the store. Her hair was crimped in black waves and she smiled with her full lips held together, stretched as far as they would go; she told you the price in a little rapping voice, daring you to challenge her and, when you did not, handed you the bag of fruit with open mockery in her eyes.

One morning in the winter I was walking up the school hill very early; a neighbour had given me a ride into town. I lived about a kilometre out of town, on a farm, and I should not have been going to the town school at all, but to a country school nearby where there were half a dozen pupils and a teacher a little demented since her change of life. But my mother, who was an ambitious woman, had prevailed on the town trustees to accept me and my father to pay the extra tuition, and

I went to school in town. I was the only one in the class who carried a lunch pail and ate peanut-butter sandwiches in the high, bare, mustard-coloured cloakroom, the only one who had to wear rubber boots in the spring, when the roads were heavy with mud. I felt a little danger, on account of this; but I could not tell exactly what it was.

I saw Myra and Jimmy ahead of me on the hill; they always went to school very early—sometimes so early that they had to stand outside waiting for the janitor to open the door. They were walking slowly, and now and then Myra half turned around. I had often loitered in that way, wanting to walk with some important girl who was behind me, and not quite daring to stop and wait. Now it occurred to me that Myra might be doing this with me. I did not know what to do. I could not afford to be seen walking with her, and I did not even want to—but, on the other hand, the flattery of those humble, hopeful turnings was not lost on me. A role was shaping for me that I could not resist playing. I felt a great pleasurable rush of self-conscious benevolence; before I thought what I was doing I called, "Myra! Hey, Myra, wait up, I got some Cracker Jack!" and I quickened my pace as she stopped.

Myra waited, but she did not look at me; she waited in the withdrawn and rigid attitude with which she always met us. Perhaps she thought I was playing a trick on her, perhaps she expected me to run past and throw an empty Cracker Jack box in her face. And I opened the box and held it out to her. She took a little. Jimmy ducked behind her coat and would not take any when I offered the box to him.

"He's shy," I said reassuringly. "A lot of little kids are shy like that. He'll probably grow out of it."

"Yes," said Myra.

"I have a brother four," I said. "He's awfully shy." He wasn't. "Have some more Cracker Jack," I said. "I used to eat Cracker Jack all the time but I don't any more. I think it's bad for your complexion."

There was a silence.

"Do you like Art?" said Myra faintly.

"No. I like Social Studies and Spelling and Health."

"I like Art and Arithmetic." Myra could add and multiply in her head faster than anyone else in the class.

"I wish I was as good as you. In Arithmetic," I said, and felt magnanimous.

"But I am no good at Spelling," said Myra. "I make the most mistakes, I'll fail maybe." She did not sound unhappy about this, but pleased to have such a thing to say. She kept her head turned away from me staring at the dirty snowbanks along Victoria Street, and as she talked she made a sound as if she was wetting her lips with her tongue.

"You won't fail," I said. "You are too good in Arithmetic. What are you going to be when you grow up?"

She looked bewildered. "I will help my mother," she said. "And work in the store."

"Well I am going to be an airplane hostess," I said. "But don't mention it to anybody. I haven't told many people."

"No, I won't," said Myra. "Do you read Steve Canyon in the paper?"

"Yes." It was queer to think that Myra, too, read the comics, or that she did anything at all, apart from her role at the school. "Do you read Rip Kirby?"

"Do you read Orphan Annie?"

"Do you read Betsy and the Boys?"

"You haven't had hardly any Cracker Jack," I said. "Have some. Take a whole handful."

Myra looked into the box. "There's a prize in here," she said. She pulled it out. It was a brooch, a little tin butterfly, painted gold with bits of coloured glass stuck onto it to look like jewels. She held it in her brown hand, smiling slightly.

I said, "Do you like that?"

Myra said, "I like them blue stones. Blue stones are sapphires."

"I know. My birthstone is sapphire. What is your birthstone?"

"I don't know."

"When is your birthday?"

"July."

"Then yours is ruby."

"I like sapphire better," said Myra. "I like yours." She handed me the brooch.

"You keep it," I said. "Finders keepers."

Myra kept holding it out, as if she did not know what I meant. "Finders keepers," I said.

"It was your Cracker Jack," said Myra, scared and solemn. "You bought it."

"Well you found it."

"No—" said Myra.

"Go on!" I said. "Here, I'll give it to you." I took the brooch from her and pushed it back into her hand.

We were both surprised. We looked at each other; I flushed but Myra did not. I realized the pledge as our fingers touched; I was panicky, but *all right*. I thought, I can come early and walk with her other mornings, I can go and talk to her at recess. Why not? *Why not?*

Myra put the brooch in her pocket. She said, "I can wear it on my good dress. My good dress is blue."

I knew it would be. Myra wore out her good dresses at school. Even in midwinter among the plaid wool skirts and serge tunics, she glimmered sadly in sky-blue taffeta, in dusty turquoise crepe, a grown woman's dress made over, weighted by a big empty bow at the V of the neck and folding empty over Myra's narrow chest.

And I was glad she had not put it on. If someone asked her where she got it, and she told them, what would I say?

It was the day after this, or the week after, that Myra did not come to school. Often she was kept at home to help. But this time she did not come back. For a week, then two weeks, her desk was empty. Then we had a moving day at school and Myra's books were taken out of her desk and put on a shelf in the closet. Miss Darling said, "We'll find a seat when she comes back." And she stopped calling Myra's name when she took attendance.

Jimmy Sayla did not come to school either, having no one to take him to the bathroom.

In the fourth week or the fifth, that Myra had been away, Gladys Healey came to school and said, "Do you know what—Myra Sayla is sick in the hospital."

It was true. Gladys Healey had an aunt who was a nurse. Gladys put up her hand in the middle of Spelling and told Miss Darling. "I thought you might like to know," she said.

"Oh yes," said Miss Darling. "I do know."

"What has she got?" we said to Gladys.

And Gladys said, "Akemia, or something. And she has blood transfusions." She said to Miss Darling, "My aunt is a nurse."

So Miss Darling had the whole class write Myra a letter, in which everybody said, "Dear Myra, We are all writing you a letter. We hope you will soon be better and be back to school, Yours truly …" And Miss Darling said, "I've thought of something. Who would like to go up to the hospital and visit Myra on the twentieth of March, for a birthday party?"

I said, "Her birthday's in July."

"I know," said Miss Darling. "It's the twentieth of July. So this year she could have it on the twentieth of March, because she's sick."

"But her *birthday* is in July."

"Because she's sick," said Miss Darling, with a warning shrillness. "The cook at the hospital would make a cake and you could all give a little present, twenty-five cents or so. It would have to be between two and four, because that's visiting hours. And we couldn't all go, it'd be too many. So who wants to go and who wants to stay here and do supplementary reading?"

We all put up our hands. Miss Darling got out the spelling records and picked out the first fifteen, twelve girls and three boys. Then the three boys did not want to go so she picked out the next three girls. And I do not know when it was, but I think it was probably at this moment that the birthday party of Myra Sayla became fashionable.

Perhaps it was because Gladys Healey had an aunt who was a nurse, perhaps it was the excitement of sickness and hospitals, or simply the fact that Myra was so entirely, impressively set free of all the rules and conditions of our lives. We began to talk of her as if she were something we owned, and her party became a cause; with womanly heaviness we discussed it at recess, and decided that twenty-five cents was too low.

We all went up to the hospital on a sunny afternoon when the snow was melting, carrying our presents, and a nurse led us upstairs, single file, and down a hall past half-closed doors and dim conversations. She and Miss Darling kept saying, "Sh-sh," but we were going on tiptoe anyway; our hospital demeanour was perfect.

At this small country hospital there was no children's ward, and Myra was not really a child; they had put her in with two grey old women. A nurse was putting screens around them as we came in.

Myra was sitting up in bed, in a bulky stiff hospital gown. Her hair was down, the long braids falling over her shoulders and down the coverlet. But her face was the same, always the same.

She had been told something about the party, Miss Darling said, so the surprise would not upset her; but it seemed she had not believed, or had not understood what it was. She watched us as she used to watch in the school grounds when we played.

"Well, here we are!" said Miss Darling. "Here we are!"

And we said, "Happy birthday, Myra! Hello, Myra, happy birthday!" Myra said, "My birthday is in July." Her voice was lighter than ever, drifting, expressionless.

"Never mind when it is, really," said Miss Darling. "Pretend it's now! How old are you, Myra?"

"Eleven," Myra said. "In July."

Then we all took off our coats and emerged in our party dresses, and laid our presents, in their pale flowery wrappings on Myra's bed. Some of our mothers had made immense, complicated bows of fine satin ribbon, some of them had even taped on little bouquets of imitation roses and lilies of the valley. "Here Myra," we said, "Here Myra, happy birthday." Myra did not look at us, but at the ribbons, pink and blue and speckled with silver, and the miniature bouquets; they pleased her, as the butterfly had done. An innocent look came into her face, a partial, private smile.

"Open them, Myra," said Miss Darling. "They're for you!"

Myra gathered the presents around her, fingering them, with this smile, and a cautious realization, an unexpected pride. She said, "Saturday I'm going to London to St. Joseph's Hospital."

"That's where my mother was at," somebody said. "We went and saw her. They've got all nuns there."

"My father's sister is a nun," said Myra calmly.

She began to unwrap the presents, with an air that not even Gladys could have bettered, folding the tissue paper and the ribbons, and drawing out books and puzzles and cutouts as if they were all prizes she had won. Miss Darling said that maybe she should say thank you, and the person's name with every gift she opened, to make sure she knew whom it was from, and so Myra said, "Thank you, Mary Louise, thank you, Carol," and when she came to mine she said, "Thank you, Helen." Everyone explained their presents to her and there was talking and excitement and a little gaiety, which Myra presided over, though she was not gay. A cake was brought in with

Happy Birthday Myra written on it, pink on white, and eleven candles. Miss Darling lit the candles and we all sang Happy Birthday to You, and cried, "Make a wish, Myra, make a wish—" and Myra blew them out. Then we all had cake and strawberry ice cream.

At four o'clock a buzzer sounded and the nurse took out what was left of the cake, and the dirty dishes, and we put on our coats to go home. Everybody said, "Goodbye, Myra," and Myra sat in the bed watching us go, her back straight, not supported by any pillow, her hands

resting on the gifts. But at the door I heard her call; she called, "Helen!" Only a couple of the others heard; Miss Darling did not hear, she had gone out ahead. I went back to the bed.

Myra said, "I got too many things. You take something."

"What?" I said. "It's for your birthday. You always get a lot at a birthday."

"Well you take something," Myra said. She picked up a leatherette case with a mirror in it, a comb and a nail file and a natural lipstick and a small handkerchief edged with gold thread. I had noticed it before. "You take that," she said.

"Don't you want it?"

"You take it." She put it into my hand. Our fingers touched again.

"When I come back from London," Myra said, "you can come and play at my place after school."

"Okay," I said. Outside the hospital window there was a clear carrying sound of somebody playing in the street, maybe chasing with the last snowballs of the year. This sound made Myra, her triumph and her bounty, and most of all her future in which she had found this place for me, turn shadowy, turn dark. All the presents on the bed, the folded paper and ribbons, those guilt-tinged offerings, had passed into this shadow, they were no longer innocent objects to be touched, exchanged, accepted without danger. I didn't want to take the case now but I could not think how to get out of it, what lie to tell. I'll give it away, I thought, I won't ever play with it. I would let my little brother pull it apart.

The nurse came back, carrying a glass of chocolate milk.

"What's the matter, didn't you hear the buzzer?"

So I was released, set free by the barriers which now closed about Myra, her unknown, exalted, ether-smelling hospital world, and by the treachery of my own heart. "Well thank you," I said. "Thank you for the thing. Goodbye."

Did Myra ever say goodbye? Not likely. She sat in her high bed, her delicate brown neck rising out of a hospital gown too big for her, her brown carved face immune to treachery, her offering perhaps already forgotten, prepared to be set apart for legendary uses, as she was even in the back porch at school.

Activities

1. Create a visual to represent major plot elements of the short story form, such as initial incident and rising action. After reading this story, add specific details of its plot to your visual, including positive and negative interactions that take place. Revise the visual if necessary.

2. Work with a small group. Do you agree or disagree that the narrator can be described as a dynamic character? Use information from the story to support your point of view.

3. Work with a partner. Pretend that one of you is Myra and the other is the narrator. As Myra, explain how your actions set you apart from the other students. As the narrator, summarize the lessons you learn from Myra.

4. Work with a small group. Prepare a conversation that might have taken place between one of the following: the sick girl and her parents when they come to visit, the girls after the pretend birthday party, the teacher discussing the day with a friend. Present the dialogue to the class.

My Guilt

Agnes Copithorne

Focus Your Learning
Reading this poem will
help you to:
- plan and facilitate a
  group activity
- create a talk show
- evaluate group
  procedures and set
  goals for improvement

When I was a child I walked two miles to school

accompanied by a neighbour boy two years younger.

Freddie was fat and freckle faced

with wheat-straw hair and a mean stepmother.

It was late fall and one day his father

bought him a new winter cap.

It was made of heavy brown tweed with ear flaps.

It cost one dollar and twenty cents.

The next morning when he joined me

on the way to school, he showed me his new cap.

Almost bursting with pride, he took it off

so I could see the rabbit fur lining the ear flaps.

Whether out of downright meanness, or jealousy

because I didn't have a new cap,

just last year's old red knitted toque,

I snatched it out of his hand

tossing it in the air and catching it again.

This went on for about half a mile.

Screaming and pleading, he ran after me.

But his legs were shorter than mine,

he couldn't catch me.

Winded, I stopped and thrust the cup down a badger hole.

He ran up sobbing and reached down into the earth.

But the hole was deep, his arm not long enough.

He sat back on his heels and cried bitterly.

Guiltily, I stretched my arm down,

But there was no bottom, or so it appeared.

"Come on," I said, "We'll be late for school,

we'll get it on our way home tonight."

All day I felt his troubled gaze upon me
and I had trouble focussing on the printed page.
When we trudged homeward after school,
we tried again to rescue the cap, with no success.
And since Freddie was not allowed to loiter,
nor was I, we gave up.
Freddie dragged his feet, dreading to face
his stepmother and I too cowardly
to confess my guilt.

Later that evening his father took a shovel
and dug, but the hole was deep, slanting off
in different directions underground.
He gave up too and Freddie cried himself to sleep.
After that he came to school bareheaded.
My heart was like a stone in my breast
when I looked at his ears red with cold.
But I had no money to buy him another cap
even had I wanted to, which I suppose I didn't.

They moved away after that, not because of the cap,
but drought, poverty and all that goes with it
drove them to another part of the country.
Through the many years since,
Freddie's sad face haunts me accusingly
and rightly so, for the callous thing I had done,
when I was twelve and he was ten.

Activities

1. Work with a small group. Prepare a talk show involving the narrator and Freddie, who are now older (in their late 20's), and other characters such as the mother, the father, and the teacher. Develop questions to find out about the motives for each character's actions and about the impact of the events on their lives. Present the talk show to the class. Afterwards, share ideas about what worked well in preparing and presenting the talk show, and what could be done better in the future.

Out of My Skin

TESSA
MCWATT

Caribbean Jill Walker, copyright Jill Walker, bob@caribsurf.com

October 4, 1959

Each day that lizard walks the same path across the wall at about the same time. The sun divides the room into then and now and in the blackness of now I rest in the shade. This room is at the back of the house, behind the kitchen where people chatter and gossip. The floorboards creak when I walk to the window, so I don't go to the window any more. Just as well. The squalor. The dogs destroy the yard and their scraping paws pelt our garbage at the house. Chickens run, squawking, and rough brown mud in mad chicken scratches splatters the whitewash in the rain.

If I lie still enough I can feel a breeze from the sea and smell salt mixed with cardamom from Mrs. DaSilva's spice shop. Me, as a boy, walking past her shop plugging my nose and mouth tight for fear I'd vomit right there on the road from the choking, chalky smell of powdered flavour. It was she who was responsible for my finally working at Atkinson's. She would see me with my nose plugged as I walked by and cry out: "Hey boy, don' plug up yu face like dat. Y'ain goin' no fuder dan dis block, mista you damn cheeky, too-good-for-the-rest-of-us boy." Even when I was older, she taunted me and teased me, calling me "Spice Fear Boy" every time I passed the shop. She called it out one day as Mr. Atkinson was leaving the shop and he stopped to ask me what she meant and I told him. We talked and I impressed him with my civilized behaviour and I said the right words and he knew I was going somewhere and he gave me my job.

Activities

1. Create a chart to record the images in this selection, using the headings Smell, Hearing, Taste, and Sight. How does the appeal to the reader's senses heighten the response to this piece of writing?

2. Express in your own words what the woman in the story said.

3. Write a sequel to this selection. Imagine that you are now a successful adult returning to your humble beginnings in a poor village. Explain to your grandchildren how your "civilized behaviour" got you far in life.

Dust Devil

Jeannette
Armstrong

Kwakiutl Potlatch Button Blanket

Focus Your Learning
Reading this poem will help you to:
- identify and explain how similes work effectively
- identify how word choice creates particular effects
- create illustrations

Around the corners fast swirled dust
whirled past the mourners; slowing,
just brushing the raw torn ground;
growing in might and rushing
a sound through the eaves, like a foghorn
blowing its way through the night; lifting leaves
then quietly sifting down, a fine grey cloud,
shrouding the hushed crowd and the town.

Activities

1. What is a dust devil? What simile does the author use to describe the sound of it? Is it effective? Can you think of another simile that might work effectively to describe the sound of the dust devil?

2. Work with a small group. Read the poem aloud and notice all the words that end in "-ing." As a group, discuss why you think the author uses so many of these words.

3. Create an illustration for this poem, using thought bubbles to record some thoughts that the mourners might be having about the deceased and the reasons for the appearance of the dust devil.

Some Tings Lie So Deep

DENISE
BARNARD

Focus Your Learning

Reading this story will help you to:
- summarize main ideas
- draft, appraise, and revise a piece of writing
- identify the use of metaphors
- create an original illustration and caption
- plan and create a role play

The way we stand, my mother and I, side by side at the kitchen counter, reminds me

of the experiments we carried out in high school science class. We are conducting an experiment of a different kind. Ours spans generations—the ones long dead and those yet to be born.

Lesson #1: "We call it pepper pot. Not because it full up o' pepper, mekking it too hot for our mout. Maybe we just do it to be extra, what you call showin' off. The other islands call it callaloo. But I always prefer pepper pot. Me no know why." Mama says all this, as if trying to explain why she likes the color red better than blue.

"I can't mama. I can't eat anymore. Please don't make me."

"Eh, eh. But what is dis? Ain't got no room for me food, dis food me slave over, but you never tired o' eatin' dem hot dogs, hamburgers, french fries, dem people's food. Wha' happen? You forget where you born? You gon' eat it even if it kill you."

But what's wrong with their food? Why do we have to do everything differently? You can buy a hot dog anywhere, but where can you find plantain and codfish?

Mama pats her stomach and smiles. "We love our food back home. Not because we greedy guts, 'cause is only time we all be together. We laugh, talk, sing, shout, most of all eat."

The history of food weights heavily upon my mother—in the fifty pounds she's been struggling to lose for as long as I can remember. "Me try and try, but me no can." Thanks to her greedy cancer, she's having no trouble these days.

Lesson #2: "Best way to describe dis is a mess o' greens. A bit o' dis, a bit o' dat. We take anyting we can find … edo top, dasheen leaves, spinach, eggplant, broccoli, green peas, cabbage. All dat give it body. But you got to dress dat body up wid someting. Start wid salted meat to give it dat just-so taste and end up wid dumplings and okra for dat final someting-in-your-mout taste."

"But how much of each do you add?" I ask.

"Me no have no recipe. Me just know. It all heh in me head and hands. Nobody know nothin' for sure in dese countries."

I can still remember myself as an innocent twelve-year-old, sharing secrets with my first boyfriend behind the school, only a block from home.

"My name isn't really Julie."

"What is it?" A gaze filled with sudden interest.

"Jewel." Another pause. Longer than the first.

"Good thing you picked Julie. Jewel sounds like one of those names on the soap operas my mom loves watching. My dad says they're garbage." Stated matter-of-factly, proudly in fact. Too stupid to know he'd hurt my feelings.

"You're right. Besides, no one calls me that except for my mom," I said, trying to keep the tremor in my voice from showing. "I … better go before my mama wonders where I am." A hasty good-bye and then a mad dash.

"Hey Julie, do you want to meet tomorrow?" His eager voice bridging the distance, but I pretended not to hear.

Quiet at dinner, until mama said, "Jewel, what got your mout shut so tight tonight?" Throwing my name in my face one too many times.

"Mama, you know that's not my name. It's Julie. A jewel is something you buy in a gem shop."

"And here me did tink you was de only jewel I was gon' have. What a way I is a fool. Since when your name change, young lady?"

"Since now. When I'm older, I'm going to change it for real."

Measure. Measure up. Is that what I've been taught to do my whole life? Measure myself against everyone, everything else. Is that what living in this country has taught me? Although this new world is not the first I discovered, I realize how firmly rooted I am in this soil. But surely I was someone there, someone other than the person I became here. Who has taught me to measure myself against my mother's wishes?

Suddenly, I feel an expectant gaze burning into my back. I turn to meet my mother's eyes.

"Julie, you listenin' to a word me sayin'?"

Lesson #3: If you no soak de beef or pig's tail overnight, you not gon' get enough flavor, and no matter wha' you do, your pepper pot not gon' turn out right. You boil all de greens till dey just pieces and den mash dem until dey fine-fine."

She stands there, hand on hip, all knowing. For a second,

appearing the way she always seemed to me as a child. When I was eight or nine, coming home from school annoyed. Annoyed that Mrs. DeGroot had asked me to do my geography project on another country, not Canada.

"Julie, your mother tells me you're from Antigua. I'm sure the class would like to learn more about this place. I know I would." But I didn't. A place I could hardly remember. A place I sometimes wanted to forget.

Mama's cure for what ailed me? A secret I didn't understand.

"Some tings lie so deep in you, no way can ignore dem. Sooner or later, dey find you wedder you ready or not."

Then, when she thought she'd consoled me sufficiently, mama said with a grin, "Besides, me carry you in dey," pointing to her belly, "and me still have de marks for prove it, so no way you ever gon' lost, no matter wha' you do."

I know it would not take much to transform her stubborn brow into an uncertainty; perplexed and uncomprehending at first, later, frightened. But all I want to know is if my mother is happy with her life, feels it's complete, as we stand here, caught up in a moment that surely we will never have again. But this is not the time or the place.

My mother catches my stare out of the corner of her eye and throws it back to me without saying a word.

Lesson #4: Okra is de important ingredient. We use it in many dishes, even add it when we turnin' fungi. There's nothin' like pepper pot. Slimy when it cook, full up o' seeds, floatin' on de sea o' green, remindin' me o' de salt water back home. Always time for pepper pot, all year round. When me feelin' ache for where me born, specially on dem nasty winterin' days, seemin' more everyday I feel dat way, all it take is a bowl o' pepper pot warmin' me belly to set me right. Don't know if many people know okra good for more dan just eatin'. When we skin get inflamed, we wet it and soothe wid okra. If we no have none o' dat, cactus, what some call prickle pear, is what we use."

"What's fungi?" I ask.

"Oh me forget. Me speakin' another language," my mother says with a grin. "To you, is cornmeal."

This sea of green that I once called 'sh—' to my mother's face, thinking I was so cool. Even as the word slid off my tongue into her unsuspecting arms, I knew I wasn't cool, and it wasn't 'sh—' either. Back then, we used the word to describe anything we thought was ugly or just didn't like. Jimmy Papanouos, a boy in my class, thought it was a good way to describe my skin ... to describe me. The only thing that kept me from crying was his forced humiliation by Mrs. Williams in front of the class after self-appointed snitch Jennifer Best told on him. Mrs. Williams twisted his ear until it burned as brightly as his face, and he was only too quick to apologize. Even after she said, "It's the differences that make Canada what it is. We can all learn something from one another," I didn't feel any better; in fact, I felt worse. It wasn't long afterward that I dropped Gracie, a coolie girl from Trinidad, as my best friend, and started hanging out with Jen.

My mother would not have understood why I just sat there and took it, letting him call me that, instead of "cussing him out," had I the courage to tell her. Instead, I decided to drop that bomb of shame on her. The shock and pain of her hand across my cheek split my pride in two and from the fissure came tears, tears I'd been holding back for much too long.

"Mama, I'm sorry."

"Julie, me don' want to hear it. Get out of me sight, until you come back to de senses God give you. To tink I workin' for dis, for you." As she walked away, her back clenched tight as a fist, it was easy to mistake hurt for anger. Especially since she did not speak to me for two days afterward. We have not spoken about it since.

Lesson #5: "These tings we call dumplings, we also call drops, because we drop dem in de pepper pot for de last. But when we finish and sittin' down to eat, dem drops is like presents, like de first we fin' on Christmas morn when I was a girl. Me save dem to de last so I

have one final treat before me finish. Seem to make it taste better somehow. Me always wonder how a bit o' dis (flour and water) and a bit o' dat (salt) taste so good. But me mother always say, 'You only need a little bit o' nothin' to make a whole lot o' somethin'.'"

I watch my mother knead the dough until it is a bloated work of art. As she rolls it, I stand hypnotized by the quick action of her fingers, until my mind is as smooth as the pasty tablet. She tears off a handful and gives it to me. Together we roll the short stubby fingers in silence, our arms making contact every so often. We toss our drops into the sea, before taking our seats at the table. Mama starts to crochet, her concentration cast into every stitch; I stare out the window, at nothing at all, until I am far, far away.

Pride has always been a delicate matter between my mother and I. "Mama, you know what the doctor said, you're going to have to cut out certain foods. He suggested you even try some of the weight-loss meals. They'll be better for you than ..."

"He no know a who he talkin'. What me want wid dat?" mama said, looking to me for an answer. Finding none, she turned away, claiming my frustration as her own, sucking it in through her teeth and tongue and unleashing a rasp of disapproval. Bending over the open face of a rumbling pot, mama exhaled a beaded mist that coated her with moisture and left her eyes weeping. "Why we want look like dese people? Pale, sickly, skin and bone some o' dem. Me a cassava and yam woman. Our food make us strong, healthy, ready for anyting. How many able to say dat?"

But are we ever really ready for anything?

"Julie, you no gon' check on de pepper pot," mama says suddenly, as if the thought has just occurred to her. But she is much too calm, her eyes fastened on her diligent hands.

"How will I know ..." I ask.

"Use your nose. Dat's what it for."

I stand, head bowed in silence, my nose poised over the spitting contents, divining with each breath its readiness, leaning further into that mess, until I am lost in it, part of it, and cannot find my way out. I imagine eating the disease right out of my mother with every mouthful I will take, until I am sick to my stomach. The steam scorches my tears before they even have a chance to lend their salty flavor to the pepper pot. Just when I am about to evaporate, disappear ...

"Julie, why you no pay more attention to what you a do for a change? The pepper pot a burn up under your nose." And then, as if she can read my thoughts, the way she seemed to when I was young, she says, her hand on my shoulder and her mouth at my ear, "Buck up Julie, we can always make another pot."

Activities

1. Work with a partner. Discuss what each "Lesson" teaches about life. Summarize your conclusions for the class.

2. Work with a partner. Write a first draft of a paragraph explaining how the cooking lessons help the mother and daughter communicate. Include short quotes from the story that support your ideas. Share the draft with your partner and help each other edit. Write a final draft of your paragraph.

3. Identify as many metaphors in the story as you can. Choose and illustrate your favourite one to show its meaning visually. Add a caption, briefly explaining why you think the author chose this metaphor.

4. Work with a partner. Look carefully at "Lesson #4," where Jewel writes that she "decided to drop the bomb of shame" on her mother but does not explain further. Create a role play in which Jewel tells her mother about her shame. Present your role play to the class.

You Have Two Voices

Nancy Prasad

Taken from *Who Hides in the Park?* ©1986 Warabe Aska, published by Tundra Books.

Focus Your Learning

Reading this poem will help you to:

- use a graphic organizer to organize ideas
- draft, appraise, and revise a piece of writing
- identify the use of simile and metaphor
- create an illustration

You have two voices when you speak

in English or your mother tongue.

When you speak the way your people spoke

the words don't hesitate but flow

like rivers, like rapids, like oceans of sound,

and your hands move like birds through the air.

But then you take a stranger's voice

when you speak in your new tongue.

Each word is a stone dropped in a pool.

I watch the ripples and wait for more.

You search in vain for other stones to throw.

They are heavy. Your hands hang down.

You have two voices when you speak;

I have two ears for hearing.

Speak to me again in your mother tongue.

What does it matter how little I understand

when the words pour out like music

and your face glows like a flame.

Activities

1. Work with a partner. Use a graphic organizer to compare the two voices in the poem. Use this information to write a first draft of a paragraph that compares the two ways of speaking, including the use of simile and metaphor. Share your draft with your partner and help each other edit. Write a final draft of your paragraph.

2. Create an illustration of the person in the poem to show how he/she speaks in two ways.

All Our Worldly Goods Peter Ginter

Activities

1. Look carefully at the background of the
    photograph. List as many details as you
    can find. What sense or feeling do you
    get from the background? What does it
    tell you about the lives of the people
    who live in this area? Why did the
    photographer choose to have this as his
    background? How would the overall
    mood of the photograph change if the
    background were a wheat field, a snow-
    capped mountain range, or a fun fair?

2. Create a poem to convey the sense and
    feeling of the photograph.

3. Work with a partner. With your partner,
    write a dialogue that the man in the
    photograph might have later on as he
    tries to explain to a friend how he spent
    his evening. Present the dialogue to
    the class.

My Mother, Who Came from China, Where She Never Saw Snow

Laureen Mar

In the huge, rectangular room, the ceiling

a machinery of pipes and fluorescent lights,

ten rows of women hunch over machines,

their knees pressing against pedals

and hands pushing the shiny fabric thick as tongues

through metal and thread.

My mother bends her head to one of these machines.

Her hair is coarse and wiry, black as burnt scrub.

She wears glasses to shield her intense eyes.

A cone of orange thread spins. Around her,

talk flutters harshly in *Toisan wah*.

Chemical stings. She pushes cloth

through a pounding needle, under, around, and out,

breaks thread with a snap against fingerbone, tooth.

Sleeve after sleeve, sleeve.

It is easy. The same piece.

For eight or nine hours, sixteen bundles maybe,

250 sleeves to ski coats, all the same.

It is easy, only once she's run the needle

through her hand. She earns money

by each piece, on a good day,

thirty dollars. Twenty-four years.

It is frightening how fast she works.

She and the women who were taught sewing

terms in English as Second Language.

Dull thunder passes through their fingers.

Activities

1. Work with a group. Discuss how the title is connected to the content of the poem. Also talk about the meaning of *irony* and how it is present in the title. Summarize and present your responses to the class.

2. Imagine that the poet has just found a journal that her mother wrote as she waited to catch the boat to North America. Write the journal entry that the poet came across. Consider the following questions as you write: What was the mother dreaming about as she was leaving China? What hopes might she have had for her new life?

3. Work with a partner. List images that describe how the mother and the other women might be feeling. Represent these images visually, reflecting the theme of the poem. Present and explain your illustrations to the class.

1. Create a booklet using the information you have recorded from mini-lessons on figurative language. Include all the terms reviewed, definitions noted down, and examples taken from selections in this section. For each term, also include an example that you create yourself. You might want to illustrate your booklet.

2. Work with a partner to create poster advertisements for each other. Begin by listing your own weak points. Then take your partner's list and rework the negatives into positives, as in "Your Hidden Skills." Create a poster using this revised information to advertise your friend as if he or she were looking for a job. Apply the advertising strategies you learned about in "Tricks of the Trade." Don't put your friend's name on the poster, however. Create a class display of all the advertisements, and challenge classmates to match names with advertisements.

3. Imagine that you are a school counsellor hired to create a brochure for teenagers on cliques and cliquishness. Work with a partner to determine what teenagers' needs are in relation to cliques. First, develop a list of interview questions to help you identify these needs. Then, interview classmates to find out about their experiences with cliquish behaviour. Finally, create the brochure, using the information from your interviews and the various selections in this section that deal with this issue. Your brochure is meant to help teenagers deal with cliquishness, both as members of cliques and as victims of them. If possible, use a page-layout program to give your brochure a professional look.

4. Work with a small group. Write a dialogue between "the Beast" and Nicole from the article "Life Sentence." Your dialogue should include pre-, during-, and post-treatment sections. To show your understanding of what motivates the characters, include thoughts, feelings, and images appropriate to Nicole and the Beast. Use the library or the Internet to research more facts and details about eating disorders, and revise your script to incorporate some of your new information and understandings. If possible, prepare a video presentation of your dialogue. Present the dialogue to the class. Afterwards, discuss with your own group what went well and what you should improve for future presentations. Consult with other groups to confirm your group's self-assessment. Provide other groups with constructive feedback and suggestions for improvement.

5. Work with a small group. Begin by reading or re-reading the excerpt from the play "See Saw" included in this section, as well as a play included in one of the other sections. Next, write a list of major criteria such as dialogue and stage directions that identify plays. Then, use information from the article "Handling Anger and Resolving Conflict" to develop a script that shows characters using the same techniques for handling anger. Once your script has been developed according to the criteria, practise your play with a small group and perform it for the class.

6. Re-read selections in this section that contain new or difficult words. Create a vocabulary list of these words. First, try to guess the meaning of each word by using the context (the sentence or passage) in which it appears. Then, check the word in a dictionary. Compare your guessed meaning with the dictionary version. Adjust your definition as necessary. Write sentences in which you use each word correctly.

7. Use the story "Day of the Butterfly" to create a picture book for younger children. Start by creating brief summaries of the major parts of the story and identifying the important scenes that you will illustrate. Draft illustrations for these scenes and text to go with them. Have a classmate review your draft and offer constructive suggestions for improvement. Prepare the final copy and present it to younger students in a local elementary school. As a class, prepare an evaluation guide for the elementary class to use for a written or oral response to your book.

8. Pick your favourite piece in this section. Find a visual in a book, magazine, or on the Internet that you think relates to the theme or mood of your chosen piece. Prepare a short oral presentation explaining why you believe that your visual should be included with the piece. Make your presentation to the class or a small group.

look back

How does where you've been affect where you're going? Can you turn back...or only look back?

▚ ▚ ▚

Get out your compass and
point it to the past.
Then you can see how the
past has led you.

How the Opossum Stole Fire

A legend of the Cora Indians of western Mexico

RETOLD BY
FERNANDO
BENÍTEZ

Focus Your Learning
Reading this legend
will help you:
- make connections
  between your
  own experiences
  and the text
- understand the
  genre of legend
- create a legend

Long ago, people did not know what fire was. They
lived on the roots of plants, sagebrush seeds, and
animal meat, all of which they ate raw. They had to eat everything
without cooking it.

Our ancestors, the Great Ones as they are called in the
Tabaosimoa language, met together and discussed how they could go
about finding something that could warm them and with which they
could cook their food. They debated it day and night. They even fasted
and slept apart from their wives. Every day they saw the great fire that
came out of the east, passed over their heads, and then went down
into the sea, but they were never able to touch it.

The Great Ones grew tired and finally called together all the
peoples and animals of the earth.

"Brothers," they told them, "would any of you be able to bring us
the fire that passes overhead every day?"

"Well," said one of the men, "five of us could go to the east
where the sun rises and steal one of its rays, just one shaft of light
from the fire in the sky that warms us every day."

"That sounds like a good idea," replied the Great Ones. "So it
shall be. Let five men go to the east. We will stay here fasting and
praying. Perhaps they will succeed in wresting a ray of light away from
the sun, and we'll finally have what we've needed for so long."

Five men immediately set out and at last came to the hill from
which the fire arose. They waited there for dawn. But when daylight
came, they realized that the sun actually rose behind a second hill
beyond the first one, so they continued their journey to the east.

When they arrived at the second hill, they saw that the sun
seemed to come up behind a third hill that was much farther away.
And thus they continued on, to a fourth and finally a fifth hill before
they became discouraged and returned to the others, sad and tired.

"O Great Ones," they said. "We have travelled from hilltop to
hilltop in pursuit of the sun, and we know now that we will never be
able to catch up to it. This is why we're so sad. Sad and defeated."

"That's all right. You've carried out what you offered to do. Now you may rest. We will continue to think of how we might go about reaching the sun. We beg you with all our hearts to help us with your prayers and wise counsel."

Then Yaushu, the wise opossum, stepped forward. "Listen to me, O Great Ones! Once I travelled to the east and saw a light far away. I asked myself, 'What is that shining so brightly over there, at the farthest edge of my sight? I have to find out.'"

"So I travelled toward it day and night. I gave up sleeping and almost gave up eating. I no longer thought about weariness. At the end of the fifth day, I saw a circle of logs burning at the entrance to an enormous cave. Flames from the fire leaped high into the air and gave off whirlwinds of sparks. An old man sat on a small bench, watching the circle of fire. He was tall and wore no clothes other than a loincloth of jaguar skin. His hair stood on end and his eyes gleamed fearfully. From time to time he would get up and throw branches and logs onto the blaze. I was afraid and hid behind a tree without daring to get any closer. Then, ever so slowly, I crept away. As I moved farther off from the circle of light, the heat grew less intense. 'It's something hot,' I said to myself. 'Something terrible and dangerous.' That was what I saw in the east, lords and fathers."

"And would you, Yaushu, be willing to return to that cave and bring us back a ray of that wonderful light?" asked the Great Ones.

"Yes, I am willing to go back there. But before I do, brothers and sisters, I ask you to fast for five days and pray to the gods for help and give them offerings of corn flour and cotton."

"We will do as you ask," said the Great Ones. "But you must know, Yaushu, that if you deceive us, we will kill you."

Yaushu smiled at them and said nothing. The Great Ones fasted for five days. As they did so, they continuously begged the gods to grant Yaushu what he had desired for so many long years. When their fast was over, they gave Yaushu five bags of corn flour with sage seeds.

"I'll be back soon," the opossum told them. "If all goes well, it should take about five days. Wait for me until after midnight. Put sleep aside and stay wide awake. There's a chance I might die. If that happens, please don't mourn or think back on me."

After saying this, Yaushu set off with the five bags of corn flour on his back. Five days later he found the same old man he had once seen, sitting on his bench and looking into the fire.

"Good evening, Grandfather," said Yaushu.

The old man did not answer.

"Good evening, Grandfather," Yaushu said again.

"What are you doing running around at this hour?" the Lord of Fire asked him.

"The elders, the Great Ones that live down below, have asked me to bring them some holy water."

"Why didn't you come earlier? This isn't the right time," said the old man.

"I'm the Great Ones' messenger," replied Yaushu. "I'm very tired, and all I ask is that you let me sleep a bit here. By dawn tomorrow, I'll be on my way."

After pleading with the old man in his high little voice and using all his powers of persuasion, Yaushu finally convinced the Lord of Fire to let him bed down just outside the cave.

"All right. You can spend the night here, but don't touch anything," the old man warned him.

Yaushu sat down near the fire. He mixed some corn flour with water from the gourd he carried, dished it out onto two plates, and offered one of them to the Lord of Fire.

"If you're hungry, let me invite you to eat with me, even though my provisions are getting low and I still have a long way to go."

The old man smelled the corn flour, and the aroma went straight to his heart. He took the plate Yaushu offered him and poured a bit of the corn flour into the middle of the fire. Then he put his finger into the flour and water on his plate and picked up a bit of the paste. He threw a few drops of it over his shoulder and a few more on the ground. Then he began to eat. When he had finished, he gave the plate back to Yaushu.

"That corn meal of yours is quite tasty," he said. "It fills you right up, too. May God bless you for sharing it with me. *She timua, tamashiten.*"

Yaushu stretched out his blanket a short distance from the cave. He was trying to think of some way he could steal a bit of the fire. After a while, he began to snore. Then the old man laid out a dried animal skin and rested his head on a rock. A short time later he got up, bowed to the fire, and stirred up the flames. Then he lay down to rest again. The animal skin beneath him creaked for a few moments as he settled himself, and soon after that, he also began to snore.

Yaushu hit the ground several times with his foot. When he was sure the old man was sleeping, he slid silently out of bed and crept up to the fire. Then he reached out his tail, picked up a burning ember, and slowly backed away into the night.

He had gone quite a distance when a gale of wind swooped down upon him. The trees bent under its force; stones rolled along the ground. Yaushu ran as hard as he could, but the wind caught up to him and suddenly the Lord of Fire stood before him, trembling with rage.

"Grandson, what have you done? I warned you not to touch anything, and yet you chose to steal from your grandfather. Now it's too late, and you must die."

The Lord of Fire picked up Yaushu in his powerful hands and tried to wrest the ember from his grip. Even though the hot coals burned his tail, Yaushu did not let it go. The burning brand was like part of his body itself. The Lord of Fire stomped on him, crushed his bones, carried him up into the air and shook him, and finally threw him back down on the earth. Then, certain he had killed him, the old man returned to his cave to take care of the fire.

Yaushu rolled down the mountainside, covered in blood, throwing off sparks like a ball of fire. That was the shape he was in when he got back to the Tabaosimoa, who were still praying. More dead than alive, he unrolled his charred tail and let the embers fall to the ground. The Great Ones picked them up and lit their hearth fires.

People all around called the opossum "Yaushu the Brave," in recognition of having brought fire to humankind from the east. To this day, the fur has never grown back on his tail, and he still walks laboriously ever since that time when Grandfather Fire, with his terrible power, broke all his bones.

Activities

1. Imagine you experience a power blackout for twenty-four hours. During this time, you have no access to fire. What effects would the blackout have on your shelter and food? Record your imaginary experiences in a personal journal entry.

2. Work in a small group to brainstorm ways in which fire could have been discovered in ancient times. Then discuss how your suggestions might be related to this legend. Present your conclusions to the class.

3. This legend explains why opossums look the way they do. In a small group, create a legend to explain one of the following: how the zebra got its stripes, how the leopard got its spots, or how the raccoon got its mask. Present your legend to the class.

4. Research another legend or myth about the origins of fire. Make a chart comparing the legend you have found with the legend of the opossum. Then write a sentence or two explaining what you have found from your comparison about the nature of legends.

What I Learned From

Raoul Wallenberg

TEXT AND PHOTOGRAPHS BY
TOM VERES

In the summer of 1944, Hitler began to kill the Jews in Hungary, as he had done in other European countries the Nazis had conquered. In July of that summer, a young Swedish architect, Raoul Wallenberg, arrived in Budapest, Hungary's capital, sent by the Swedish government. Wallenberg had no diplomatic training; his weapons were his wit and determination. His purpose was to save lives.

The day I found out what it really meant to be Wallenberg's photographer was November 28, 1944, when his secretary handed me a piece of paper with his instructions: "Meet me at Jozsefvárosi train station. Bring your camera."

The Jozsefvárosi train station was a freight depot on the outskirts of town. I took my Leica and got on the streetcar, not knowing what to expect. At the time, everybody, especially those on the Nazis' hit list, thought lying low was the best plan. Yet here I was, on a raw November morning, heading for Jozsefvárosi Station.

I found the station surrounded by Hungarian Nazis and gendarmes from the countryside. Wallenberg expected me to find a way to get in, so I shoved my camera in my pocket and went to one of the gendarmes. Using the world's phoniest Swedish accent, I spoke in a mixture of broken Hungarian and German. "I'm a Swedish diplomat! I must go in to meet Raoul Wallenberg!"

The gendarme stared at me incredulously but let me in. The scene inside was harrowing. Thousands of men were being loaded into cattle cars. Wallenberg was there with his Studebaker and his driver, Vilmos Langfelder. When he saw me, he walked over and whispered slowly, "Take as many pictures as you can."

Pictures? Here? If I were caught, I'd be on that train myself, Swedish legation or no Swedish legation. I climbed into the back seat of the car and took out my pocketknife. Cutting a small slit in my scarf, I positioned the camera inside it. Then, as calmly as possible, I walked through the train yard snapping pictures.

Wallenberg had his black ledger out. "All my people get in line here!" he called. "All you need to do is show me your Schütz-Pass!"

He approached a line of "passengers." "You, yes, I have your name here. Where is your paper?" The startled man emptied his pockets, looking for a paper he never had. He pulled a letter out. "Fine." Wallenberg said quickly. "Next!"

Men caught on at once. Letters, eyeglass prescriptions, even deportation notices became passports to freedom. In his ledger Raoul and his assistants carefully checked

---

At left (p. 152), released prisoners saved from deportation by Raoul Wallenberg walk hurriedly out of Jozsefvárosi Station on their way to freedom. Tom Veres took this photo with his camera hidden in a scarf. Veres later took each released prisoner's photo for a Schütz-Pass (p. 154), which provided safe passage out of Hungary. Raoul Wallenberg, photographed by Veres in 1944 (p. 156), was arrested with his driver by the Soviet secret police in January 1945. According to Soviet authorities, Wallenberg died of a heart attack in a Moscow prison in 1947.

off, or added, each name in the book. I tried to become invisible, snapping away, trying to catch what was going on.

"Tommy! Tommy!"

I heard my name and turned around. In line, almost on the train, was my best friend, George. We had been in Grade One together and had been friends ever since. Now he was in line to die. I had only a split second to think.

Tom Veres

I walked over, grabbed him by the collar and said, "You dirty Jew, get over there!" I pointed toward Wallenberg's line. "I said go! Are you deaf?" I kicked his backside. He understood and got in line.

Wallenberg had pulled hundreds out of line, when he sensed the Nazis losing patience. "Now back to Budapest, all of you!" he said.

The new "Swedes" walked out of the station to freedom. Wallenberg turned back to face their captors. He began to lecture them in measured tones about health conditions, crowding on trains—anything to take their attention off those departing.

As soon as they had a good head start, Raoul and I got back into the car where Vilmos waited. The danger we'd been in didn't hit me until then. This man, a *Swede*, could have waited the war out in safety, yet here he was marching into train yards surrounded by Nazis—and asking others to do the same!

When we got back to town, I found George, took him to one of Wallenberg's protected houses, and took his picture for a Schütz-Pass. "Stay here until I get your papers!" I said.

The next day, word came: more deportations from Jozsefvárosi Station. Again I was asked to go. It was a ghastly repeat. Gendarmes with machine guns; thousands being herded into trains.

This time my Leica was already hidden in the folds of my scarf. As Wallenberg started calling off common names that many men might answer to, I started snapping photos.

That day my cousin Joseph was among those marked for death, as was one of Hungary's great actors. I pulled them out of line to join Wallenberg's hundreds.

It was then that I saw a chance. I walked around the train, to the side away from the station. The train hadn't yet been padlocked from that side. I climbed on the outside of an already filled car, pushing all my weight against the bolt that held the door shut. The spring clicked. The long door slid back.

Those inside, who a moment before had stood prisoners in the darkness, now blinked at the November sky. "Move!" I said. "Quickly!" They started jumping off the train, running to the line where Wallenberg continued to give out passes.

Before long, however, Wallenberg clearly saw that his time was up and began shouting, "All of you released by the Hungarian government, back to town! March!"

At the same time, a Hungarian policeman had seen what I was up to. He pointed his revolver at me. "You!" he shouted. "Stop what you're doing!"

Raoul and his driver got into the Studebaker and drove around to my side of the train. Raoul opened the door and leaned out. "Tom! Jump!"

I didn't have a moment to think. I made the longest jump of my life.

Raoul pulled me inside, and Vilmos stepped on the gas. Raoul smiled and looked back at the train station. "I don't think we'll come back here for a while!"

Refuge in Canada

For some immigrants, the most important address in Canada is 52 Elgin Avenue in Toronto, headquarters for the Quaker Committee for Refugees. To this old brick house come individuals and families fleeing persecution in El Salvador, Iran, Bulgaria, and other countries torn by political strife. Some arrive with no more information than a slip of paper with the refugee centre's phone number written on it.

Many refugees come because they have heard of the woman who lives at 52 Elgin Avenue. She is Nancy Pocock, eighty-three years old, the centre's founder and energetic co-ordinator. Pocock and her staff of volunteers find food, shelter, and clothing, arrange help from lawyers and social workers, and guide the newcomers through the complicated immigration process. They obtain emergency legal assistance for the most desperate refugees, those in danger of deportation.

Volunteers who work with Nancy describe her as an honest and down-to-earth person with a good sense of humour. "She acts on her beliefs on a daily basis," says one volunteer. "She's the most warm and loving person I've ever met."

Nancy Pocock's work on behalf of refugees has become well known in Toronto. Many cab drivers have heard of her and take refugees right to her house. She has received numerous awards, including the Pearson Peace Medal from the United Nations Association of Canada. More important to Nancy than the awards, however, is the love extended to her from those she has helped.

Tom Veres

Some have stayed on at the centre as volunteers. For them and for thousands of others who have passed through her home, Nancy Pocock has become known affectionately as "Mama Nancy."

Activities

1. Work in a small group to make a list of some modern heroes. Why are these people heroic? How has their behaviour had an impact on the lives of others? Make a list of heroic figures who have made an impact on others. Share your list with the class, explaining your choices.

2. Imagine that you are Raoul Wallenberg. The war is over. Prepare a dramatic monologue in which you explain to your grandchildren what you did to save Jews from going to the concentration camps, and why you did it.

3. Work in a group to create a tableau of any scene described in this article. Try to catch the atmosphere captured by Tom Veres.

Carrying the Running-Aways

An African-American folk tale

RETOLD BY
VIRGINIA HAMILTON

The Underground Railroad Charles T. Webber

This painting depicts fugitives arriving at Jeri and Catharine Coffin's Ohio farm. Three thousand refugees were sheltered here before they were sent on to Canada.

Focus Your Learning

Reading this folk tale will help you:

- understand a character's motives
- identify the tone of the text
- retell a fairy tale from a first-person point of view
- recognize the legacy of oral tradition in handing down family stories

Never had any idea of carryin the runnin-away slaves over the river. Even though I was right there on the plantation, right by that big river, it never got in my mind to do somethin like that. But one night the woman whose house I had gone courtin to said she knew a pretty girl wanted to cross the river and would I take her. Well, I met the girl and she was awful pretty. And soon the woman was tellin me how to get across, how to go, and when to leave.

Well, I had to think about it. But each day, that girl or the woman would come around, ask me would I row the girl across the river to a place called Ripley. Well, I finally said I would. And one night I went over to the woman's house. My owner trusted me and let me come and go as I pleased, long as I didn't try to read or write anythin. For writin and readin was forbidden to slaves.

Now, I had heard about the other side of the river from the other slaves. But I thought it was just like the side where we lived on the plantation. I thought there were slaves and masters over there, too, and overseers and rawhide whips they used on us. That's why I was so scared. I thought I'd land the girl over there and some overseer didn't know us would beat us for bein out at night. They could do that, you know.

Well, I did it. Oh, it was a long rowin time in the cold, with me worryin. But pretty soon I see a light way up high. Then I remembered the woman told me to watch for a light. Told me to row to the light, which is what I did. And when I got to it, there were two men. They reached down and grabbed the girl. Then one of the men took me by the arm. Said, "You about hungry?" And if he hadn't been holdin me, I would of fell out of that rowboat.

Three Great Abolitionists William H. Johnson

This 1945 painting by African-American artist William H. Johnson depicts the legendary John Brown, Frederick Douglass, and Abraham Lincoln.

Well, that was my first trip. I was scared for a long time after that. But pretty soon I got over it as other folks asked me to take them across the river. Two and three at a time, I'd take them. I got used to makin three or four trips every month.

Now it was funny. I never saw my passengers after that first girl. Because I took them on the nights when the moon was not showin, it was cloudy. And I always met them in the open or in a house with no light. So I never saw them, couldn't recognize them, and couldn't describe them. But I would say to them, "What you say?" And they would say the password. Sounded like "Menare." Seemed the word came from the Bible somewhere, but I don't know. And they would have to say that word before I took them across.

Well, there in Ripley was a man named Mr. Rankins, the rest was John, I think. He had a "station" there for escaping slaves. Ohio was a free state, I found out, so once they got across, Mr. Rankins would see to them. We went at night so we could continue back for more and to be sure no slave catchers would follow us there.

Mr. Rankins had a big light about thirty feet high up and it burned all night. It meant freedom for slaves if they could get to that bright flame.

I worked hard and almost got caught. I'd been rowin fugitives for almost four years. It was in 1863 and it was a night I carried twelve runnin-aways across the river to Mr. Rankins'. I stepped out of the boat back in Kentucky and they were after me. Don't know how they found out. But the slave catchers, didn't know them, were on my trail. I ran away from the plantation and all who I knew there. I lived in the fields and in the woods. Even in caves. Sometimes I slept up in the tree branches. Or in a hay pile. I couldn't get across the river now, it was watched so closely.

Finally, I did get across. Late one night me and my wife went. I had gone back to the plantation to get her. Mr. Rankins had him a bell by this time, along with the light. We were rowin and rowin. We could see the light and hear that bell, but it seemed we weren't gettin any closer. It took forever, it seemed. That was because we were so scared and it was so dark and we knew we could get caught and never get gone.

Well, we did get there. We pulled up there and went on to freedom. It was only a few months before all the slaves was freed.

We didn't stay on at Ripley. We went on to Detroit because I wasn't takin any chances. I have children and grandchildren now. Well, you know, the bigger ones don't care so much to hear about those times. But the little ones, well, they never get tired of hearin how their grandpa brought emancipation to loads of slaves he could touch and feel in the dark but never ever see.

Activities

1. Imagine that you are the narrator taking enslaved people to freedom. What thoughts run through your mind? Use thought bubbles to record what you are saying to yourself.

2. With a partner, prepare to read selected parts of this story aloud. Be sure to read with expression appropriate to the scenes described.

3. Rewrite a well-known fairy tale, such as *Cinderella* or *Jack in the Beanstalk*, telling the story from the main character's point of view. Then, as a class, discuss what difference this makes to the story.

4. The oral tradition is the telling of history through stories related by one generation to another. Record one of your relatives talking about an important event in your family's history. Then, in your personal journal, explain what you learned about history in general and what you learned about your family from the recording.

Mandela   BILL SCHILLER

There was a time when Nelson Mandela might have been forgotten.

For more than twenty years, not a single word ever emanated from his prison cell and only one photograph of him had ever been smuggled out.

The international community might have been forgiven for allowing his name to slip from memory.

But in February 1985, that changed.

"There was a celebration at Soweto's Jabulani Stadium," Archbishop Desmond Tutu recalls in a telephone interview. The occasion was to mark Tutu's winning of the Nobel Peace Prize, which he had accepted on behalf of the South African people.

Only weeks before, the finger-waving former president of South Africa, P. W. Botha, had made a much-publicized offer to release the sixty-six-year-old Mandela, provided Mandela promised his African National Congress would lay down its arms.

In the midst of Tutu's Nobel celebration, Mandela's daughter Zindzi took the stage and startled the audience. She had a message to read from her father, she said. It was a reply to Botha's offer. The audience was rapt. Many in the stadium had not even been born when Mandela had gone to jail.

Zindzi read her father's words with pride: "I cherish my own freedom dearly, but I care even more for your freedom.

"I am not less life-loving than you are. But I cannot sell my birthright nor am I prepared to sell the birthright of the people to be free ... Only free men can negotiate.

"I cannot and will not give any undertaking at a time when I and you, the people, are not free. Your freedom and mine cannot be separated.

"I *will* return."

The crowd was stunned into silence. It was a pivotal moment.

They rose as one, sang *Nkosi Sikele-l'iAfrika* (God Bless Africa), then the black national anthem, and burst into wild, rapturous applause, ululating and dancing.

They were Mandela's first public words in two decades.

"The response was fantastic," Tutu recalls. "People probably would have understood had he jumped for Botha's bait. Having been in prison all those years, some might have thought, 'Well, here is something slightly better than jail.'

"But the response of the people was, as if to say, 'Man, he really *is* the kind of person we always believed he was.' They had not been disillusioned. He was not an idol with feet of clay."

Mandela was true to his ideals. He had not lost faith.

The long walk to freedom by the South African people, then recently revitalized by the formation of the United Democratic Front, was now supercharged.

In only a few short minutes Nelson Mandela had moved from memory, straight back into the thick of it.

And what was more incredible: he had done it all from behind bars.

It was an extraordinary accomplishment. Here was a man who had begun the early

In September 1998, Nelson Mandela led "Canada's largest-ever classroom" when he addressed 40,000 young people at SkyDome in Toronto, along with hundreds of thousand of students watching on television from classrooms across the country.

part of this century as a herd boy. Now, it was as if he had seized the bars of his cell and, in shaking them, had shaken the very pillars of the apartheid state.

He would return.

What is it that distinguishes Nelson Mandela's political leadership? What sets him apart?

Those who know him say Mandela's fabled long walk to freedom was also a long walk to leadership. He set out, quite naturally, with certain innate skills: He was genial, charming, and principled; and he was blessed with a wonderful way of communicating.

But so are many people.

One of the key ingredients that helped shape him into the extraordinary leader he is, says Tutu, is his long period of suffering behind bars.

"His leadership was forged in the furnace of adversity," says Tutu, who remains one of Mandela's greatest admirers. "I believe suffering can be a very important ingredient in leadership. I believe it deepened him."

Mandela was not born a leader. But faced with gross injustice and a lengthy prison sentence, he grew.

"You and I might easily say, 'Oh, twenty-seven years in jail! That's awful! Look at the waste,'" Tutu says. "But we can't really say that, because that suffering was actually part of the making of the man."

For every young person who has ever been criticized for being an idealist, Mandela remains the best modern-day example of a person who not only stuck to his principles and ideals, but also saw them achieved. This is why, some believe, he remains such a hero to young people today.

"Young people have an instinct for goodness," says Tutu. "They are very quick to sense humbug. That's why they are often attracted to—not successful people, necessarily; not even powerful people—but people of goodness."

In Mandela's most famous speech, delivered from the dock during the 1964 Rivonia Trial at Pretoria's Palace of Justice, he bravely put forward those principles, knowing full well that the gallows was not far away: "During my lifetime I have dedicated my life to this struggle of the African people. I have fought against white domination, and I have fought against black domination.

"I have cherished the ideal of a democratic and free society in which all persons live together in harmony with equal opportunities.

"It is an ideal which I hope to live for. But if needs be, it is an ideal for which I am prepared to die."

Mandela not only lived to see those ideals made manifest, he also helped implement them and change the face of South Africa.

My Hero Mandela

KANO MOFOKENG
(ten-year-old South African schoolboy)

My hero stands over the valley of his people fighting for them with no spear,

no gun, no knife, only the weapon of mouth and knowledge, his head held high.

The grey haired man walking out of prison not sad, not full of hatred and revenge

but smiling, laughing, laughing the laughter of his people.

There he is, the man who was imprisoned but smiling and forgiving.

There is my one and only hero Mandela.

My hero Mandela

Activities

1. Think about a time when someone you know or know about stuck to his or her principles, rather than giving in to pressure. Share your recollection with a classmate.

2. Create a circle map. In the inner circle, put the facts that you know about Nelson Mandela from reading these pieces. In the middle circle, put the inferences (conclusions you can reach based on information) that you made while reading these pieces. Then, in the outer circle, write some questions that you have about Mandela and his political movement.

3. Using a CD-ROM or print materials in the library, research answers to the questions you wrote for Activity 2.

4. Make a chart comparing the article with the poem. Which piece did you prefer? Give reasons for your choice.

Black Patent Leather Shoes

Karen L. Mitchell

Slipping into my black patent leather shoes

Not caring how many others had worn them

Or how many times they'd been

Used

Papa would make me put them on

With lace stockings

I never danced in those black leather

Shoes

Only studied their simple details:

Black

As black as my hair they surely were

With three straps, that held me there, and heels

Stacked

And I could not wear my black leather

Shoes

Every day, but only once or twice a

Week

and he would make sure black polish was

Used

Papa would make sure those shoes

Reflected me

Activities

1. In your journal, write about a time when you were all dressed up for a family occasion. Describe exactly what you were wearing, and how you were feeling at the time.

2. Draw a picture of the girl, dressed up in an outfit including the black patent leather shoes. Write a title for your drawing that captures the the emotion you imagine her to be experiencing.

3. The narrator says that "those shoes/Reflected me." Make a list of the ways in which the shoes reflected what the child was. Support your ideas with details from the poem. Share your ideas with the class.

4. Work with a partner to develop a dialogue in which a parent and a teen conflict over what the teen wants to wear and what the parent thinks is acceptable to wear. Role-play your dialogue for the class.

Messages Are

Why would a soldier's uniform have such an elaborate button? Consider what meaning this button might have for soldiers or their families. How does the image on this button relate to war and the basis for most wars?

What does the Remembrance Day poppy symbolize? What effect does wearing the poppy have on others? Think of other types of symbols we wear and what their effect might be.

Everyday packages like envelopes with stamps convey messages. What message might this envelope be conveying? What other groups are represented on envelopes, and what is the purpose of placing them there?

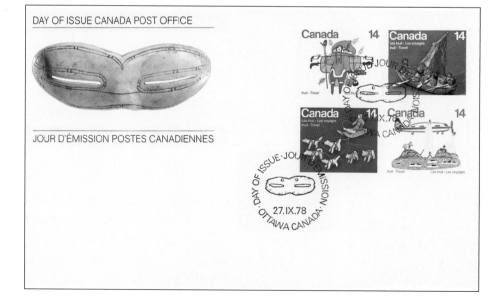

Everywhere!

In what way might this character be a hero? What are some of the ways in which we honour heroes in our culture?

"THE HERO"

ANTZ
10·2·98

PDI

www.pepsi.com/antz

DreamWorks

HATE FREE ZONE

Why would the phrase "Hate Free Zone" appear on a fridge magnet? Who needs to be protected from hate? Consider some of the ways we can create a hate free zone.

Uncovering the Rose

Archaeologists are scientists who collect information about the way people lived in the past. They excavate evidence such as buildings, graves, tools, and pottery. It is often difficult to pinpoint a site that will yield meaningful artifacts. An excavation team might search an area for years without finding anything significant. But sometimes an accident leads to an unexpected discovery …

In 1989 a construction crew in London, England, was using bulldozers to dig the foundation for a new office building. Suddenly the workers uncovered the wooden walls of an old building buried in the ground. Realizing that the walls could be important, the builders temporarily stopped construction.

Archaeologists rushed to the site to study the size, shape, and location of the structure. To their amazement, the wooden walls were the remains of a theatre used four hundred years ago by England's greatest playwright—William Shakespeare!

The theatre was called the Rose. It was built in 1587 during the Elizabethan period—named for Elizabeth I, England's reigning queen at that time. The building was quite different from the theatres of today. It was almost circular, with fourteen sides, and had a central yard that was open to the sky. For a penny each, people stood in the yard to watch a performance. Along the walls were three levels of balconies,

where people paid higher prices to sit down. Archaeologists estimate that up to two thousand people could have crammed into the theatre for a single show.

The stage was about five metres deep—smaller than most scholars had suspected. It extended into the yard so that the actors would have been almost completely surrounded by spectators. Modern actor Timothy Dalton remarked, "It's like a sixteenth-century version of television—you were that close, and [actors] could speak in conversational tones."

At the rear of the stage was a single room called the tiring house, where actors changed costumes and waited for their cues. In Shakespeare's time, all professional stage actors were men; thus, costumes and wigs were necessary for the creation of female characters. The stage itself would have had no curtain, no scenery, and very few props or pieces of furniture.

Some of the first plays written by Shakespeare—including *Henry VI*—were performed at the Rose. Many scholars also believe that Shakespeare himself acted at the Rose. Records show that Lord Strange's Company performed at the theatre in 1592, when a young William Shakespeare was a member of the troupe.

Archaeologists could study the site only from March until May, when the ruins were reburied so that construction of the office building could continue. Luckily, the new building was redesigned on giant stilts to help preserve the old.

After the surprising discovery of the Rose, British officials allowed scientists to explore a nearby site believed to be the location of the famous Globe Theatre. The Globe was built in 1599, and sixteen of Shakespeare's later plays were performed there.

In October 1989, archaeologists from the Museum of London uncovered small segments of the Globe's foundation. They also found piles of hazelnut shells. The shells seem to be evidence that four hundred years ago, audiences ate hazelnuts during a performance—just as modern film audiences eat popcorn!

Although there are no plans to build on this site, some of the remains of the Globe lie under a nineteenth-century building. The newer structure is a historical landmark and, although it is unoccupied, cannot be torn down. Excavation of the site is made even more difficult because the ruins seem to extend under a major road that leads into the centre of London.

The ruins of the Rose and the Globe may never be completely excavated, but they have given us a clearer picture of what theatre was like during the time of Shakespeare.

Activities

1. Using the information given in the article, sketch what you imagine a theatre in Shakespeare's time would have looked like.

2. Imagine that you are one of the construction workers or one of the archaeologists who worked on the site of the Rose. Document your observations and findings.

3. Research three aspects of Elizabethan theatre: casting, costumes, and sets. Prepare a short oral presentation of your findings.

4. The remains of the Rose were discovered during the construction of an office building on prime commercial land. In other cases, in Canada and elsewhere, real estate development has been delayed or stopped completely when ancient sites were discovered. As a class, debate the topic: "Ancient sites should be preserved, even at the expense of valuable real estate development."

Julius Caesar

WILLIAM SHAKESPEARE

(EXCERPT)

This famous scale model of Shakespeare's Globe Playhouse was completed by John Cranford Adams and Irwin Smith in 1954.

Cassius: Why, he that cuts off twenty years of life
Cuts off so many years of fearing death.

Brutus: Grant that, and then is death a benefit.
So are we Caesar's friends, that have abridg'd
His time of fearing death. Stoop, Romans, stoop,
And let us bathe our hands in Caesar's blood
Up to the elbows, and besmear our swords.
Then walk we forth, even to the market-place,
And waving our red weapons o'er our heads,
Let's all cry "Peace, freedom, and liberty!"

Cassius: Stoop then, and wash. How many ages hence
Shall this our lofty scene be acted over
In states unborn and accents yet unknown!

Focus Your Learning

Reading this play excerpt will help you:
- experiment with language
- identify and understand the use of irony
- appreciate word choice
- examine the motives of characters

Activities

1. Work with a partner to read this dialogue aloud several times. Then write the lines in modern English, so that the meaning is clearer to you. Compare your understanding of this scene with that of the other pairs.

2. Why do Brutus and Cassius claim they have done Caesar a favour? In modern language, write an e-mail message to Brutus and Cassius, giving your opinion of their claim.

Poet
(for Irina Ratushinskaya)

Vikram Seth

> **Focus Your Learning**
> Reading this poem will help you:
> - appreciate the imagery of a poem
> - prepare a monologue to increase your understanding of the text
> - express an idea in a variety of genres

She lived for six years in a cage. When I

Am inclined to regret the way things are, I think

Of her who through long cold and pain did not

Betray the ones she loved or plead for mercy.

They censored the few letters they allowed.

Cabbage and bread, rotten and stale, were food.

While outside governments and springs went round

And summits, thaws, and great events occurred,

Here inside was no hope. Years of her youth

Were sickened for no crime. She did not even

Know if her lover knew she was alive.

The paper she'd written poems on was removed.

What could she find?—the swirls in the cold blue light

Through bars so thick her hands could not pass through them—

Those swirls of blue light and the heels of bread

She shared with some companionable mouse.

Her poems she memorized line by line and destroyed.

The Contents were what was difficult to remember.

Activities

1. Make an organizer to record the concrete and abstract images the poet uses. Then, in a short answer response, explain why these images are effective.

2. Prepare a monologue in which this imprisoned woman tells her story.

3. Write about someone who lives life in a heroic way. Employ two of the following genres to tell the same story: an article, a poem, a speech, an interview, or a personal story. Decide which genre you like best and be prepared to explain your choice.

Why Canada Has to *Literacy* Problem

JUNE CALLWOOD

Focus Your Learning
Reading this essay will help you:
- understand how a human interest story focusses attention on a problem
- make notes to support an argument
- gather information from a video
- write a persuasive letter

Carole Boudrias shudders when she remembers the time she almost swallowed Drano because she thought it was Bromo. Even more painful to recall is the time she mistook adult pain-killers for the child-size dose and made her feverish child much sicker.

"When you can't read," she explains, "it's like being in prison. You can't travel very far from where you live because you can't read street signs. You have to shop for food but you don't know what's in most of the packages. You stick to the ones in a glass jar or with a picture on the label. You can't look for bargains because you can't understand a sign that says 'Reduced.' I would ask the clerk where is something and the clerk would say, aisle five. Only I couldn't read aisle five. I'd pretend that I was confused so they'd lead me right to the shelf."

Carole Boudrias is able to read now, at last. She's a thirty-three-year-old single parent who lives with her five children in a handsome townhouse on Toronto's harbourfront and holds a steady job. But her struggle with illiteracy is all too vivid in her memory. "You can't get a job," she says earnestly. "You can't open a bank account. You have to depend on other people. You feel you don't belong. You can't help your children. You can't help yourself."

Six years ago when her oldest child started school, the boy floundered. Because he had been raised in a household without books, print was strange to him. He would point to a word in his reader, that classic, endearingly silly *Dick and Jane,* and ask his mother what it was. She was as baffled as he, so he'd check with his teacher the next day and that evening would proudly read the new word to his mother. She began to absorb the shape of the words he identified. She found she could recognize them even days later.

That was astonishing. As a child she had been labelled mentally retarded and confined to "opportunity classes" where reading wasn't taught. She grew up believing that she wasn't intelligent enough to learn. Nevertheless, she *was* learning. The vocabulary of words she could read in her son's reader was growing. She began to think maybe the experts were wrong. Then, one miraculous day, she realized she was learning to read even faster than her son was.

"My son was my first teacher," she grins. She had never allowed herself to believe that it was possible that she could learn to read. She hadn't even tried: no one whose life is made up of poverty and failed relationships is ready to take on, voluntarily, the potential for another defeat, another kick in the self-esteem. She hesitated a long time but the evidence was persuasive—she was beginning to read. Her welfare worker had always been kind, so she summoned the nerve to ask her where she could find help.

That lead her to Beat the Street, a program that helps people who are illiterate for all the reasons that befall sad children: unrecognized learning disabilities, emotional stress, too many schools, scorn and belittling, terror, bad teachers. She was linked with a volunteer tutor, and they came to admire each other deeply.

"Now I can read, I can read books, anything. I can write. In English *and* French."

Carole Boudrias has written a book, *The Struggle for Survival,* which tells of her tortured childhood lacerated with incest and violence, and her triumphant recovery from illiteracy. Last summer she was the poet laureate of the annual golf tournament hosted by Peter Gzowski, the beloved and respected CBC broadcaster. He has befriended the cause of literacy in Canada and over the past several years has raised more than a quarter of a million dollars for Frontier College, one of the first organizations in the country to tackle the problem of illiteracy.

"Learning to read," Carole Boudrias says quietly, "was like a second birth, this time with my eyes open. Before I could read, I was a blind person."

Canada has nearly five million adult citizens who are described as functionally illiterate, which means that they can recognize a few words, such as washroom signs and exits, but they can't read dense print at all. They can't decipher directions, for instance, or application forms, or warnings on labels. The world of newspapers, posters, advertising, books, menus, banking, recipes, and instructions-for-assembly that literate people take for granted is barred to them; they live a life of bluff, anxiety, embarrassment, and isolation.

A good many Canadians are as profoundly illiterate as Carole Boudrias was.

People who meet illiterate adults are struck by the similarity of their textural experience. All of them liken the inability to read and write with being disabled or chained in a prison. Edwin Newman, an American broadcaster who writes about language, calls illiteracy "death in life."

The sense of being caged and blinded is not morbid fantasy. People who can't read may be able to walk freely but they can't go far. Subway stops rarely have pictures to guide them and the destinations bannered across the front of buses and streetcars are meaningless. If they ask for directions, well-intentioned people tell them, "Go along Main Street to Elm and turn left." Consequently, they must travel by taxi or stay home, though they usually are the poorest of the poor.

Almost every job, even simple manual labour such as street-cleaning, requires an ability to read. Personnel managers don't take kindly to people who can't fill out an application, or when asked, can't spell their own addresses.

The divide between the literate and illiterate has never been wider. In this half of the century North America has become a world of forms and documents and instructions, written warnings, posted rules, leaflets, and vital information circulated in brochures. Two generations ago, illiteracy was prevalent but not such a great disadvantage. Someone functionally illiterate could fake it through an entire lifetime and still hold a good job. Employment skills were acquired by watching someone else; apprenticeship was the accepted teacher, not two years in a community college.

Today inability to read is a ticket to social segregation and economic oblivion. A poignant example is the skilled house-painter who turned up one day in the crowded quarters of the East End Literacy Program in Toronto. He said he wanted to read. The counsellor asked him, as all applicants are asked, what he wanted to read. "Directions on paint cans," he answered promptly. "I'm losing jobs. I can't read how to mix the colours."

Many who are illiterate can't read numbers. When they are paid, they don't know if they are being cheated. Because she couldn't fill out bank deposit slips, Carole Boudrias used to cash her welfare cheque in a storefront outlet which clips poor people sharply for no-frills service. To pay for goods, she would hold out a handful of money and let the cashier take what was needed—and perhaps more, she never knew. Once she would have been shortchanged $50 she could ill afford if a stranger who witnessed the transaction hadn't protested.

The common emotional characteristic of people who can't read is depression and self-dislike. All feel at fault for their situation: with few exceptions, they went through school with bright little girls exactly their age who leaped to their feet to recite and smart little boys who did multiplication in their heads. Everyone else in the world, it seemed, could learn with ease; for them, even C-A-T looked a meaningless scribble. Teachers called them stupid; worse, so did other children.

"Stupid" may just be the cruellest word in the language. It consumes confidence, on which the ability to learn relies. Seven-year-olds having trouble with reading will frolic at recess with an edge of glee; eleven-year-olds who can't read have bitter faces and scarred souls.

Loss of hope for oneself is a descent into desolation without end. It causes men to

The divide between the literate and illiterate has never been wider.

rage in fury and women to wound themselves. People who can't read come readily to view themselves as worthless junk, and many feel they must grab what they can out of life and run. Canada's prisons are full of young men who can't read. The Elizabeth Fry Society estimates that close to ninety percent of the women in Kingston's infamous prison for women are illiterate.

Because Canada has five million people who can't read, the political shape of the country and the priorities of governments are not influenced greatly by the needs of the poor. Since illiterates are effectively disenfranchised, the political agenda is written by the more powerful. Candidates rarely find it advantageous to uphold the causes that matter most to Canada's illiterates—an end to homelessness and the need for food banks; welfare payments that meet the poverty line; and better educational and job-training opportunities. Few votes would follow any politician with such a crusade. The electorate that can't read won't be there to ruffle the complacent on election day.

Their silence costs this country severely. Education is free in Canada because it was recognized that democracy isn't healthy unless all citizens understand current events and issues. Five million Canadians can't do that. Voters, most of them literate, choose candidates who help their interests; those who don't vote, many of them illiterate, by default get a government that does not need to know they exist.

The result is a kind of apartheid. The government has lopsided representation, which results in decisions which further alienate and discourage the unrepresented. The gap between the haves and have-nots in Canada is already greater than at any time in this century, and widening. Urban apartment houses are the workplaces of crack dealers, the streets are increasingly unsafe, and households have installed electronic security systems. The poor, if asked, would have better answers than guard dogs. The best, most lasting responses to crime and addiction and violence are literacy programs, coupled with job training and full employment.

Schools are in disgrace, with a failure

rate of fully one-third of all high school students. A soup company with such a record would be out of business in a day. The educational system has managed to exacerbate the class differences which are developing in this country. Canada's millions of illiterates went through school the required number of years, give or take time out for truancy, illness, running away from abuse, and confinement in detention homes. These human discards, identified promptly in the first years of elementary schools, will ever after drift around disconsolately. They are surplus people, spare parts for which society has no use. Unless there is a war.

Carole Boudrias is working on a project, Moms in Motion, to help young mothers to get off welfare rolls. She says to them, "What do you want?" They reply, "To go back to school."

Another chance. Five million Canadians need another chance. Maybe they can become literate, maybe they can become healed and whole. What a lovely goal for the new millennium.

Activities

1. June Callwood uses strong, emotional language to describe the plight of illiterate people. Find at least three examples of this type of language. Then explain why you think she uses it.

2. Reread the article, making notes about how many people in Canada are illiterate and the effect of illiteracy on their daily lives. Work in a small group to come up with suggestions for at least five different ways of combatting illiteracy.

3. View the National Film Board's video "Ellen's Story." Compare her story of illiteracy with that of Carole Boudrias.

4. Write a letter to your local school board demanding that something be done about the high rate of illiteracy in this country. Draw on the information you gathered in Activities 2 and 3.

It's Different Now

Robert B. Foster

* ADD (Attention Deficit Disorder)—People with Attention Deficit Disorder have challenges in terms of paying attention, being hyperactive, and controlling their impulses. These difficulties are caused by having brain waves that are slightly different from the brain waves of people who don't have the disorder.

Focus Your Learning

Reading this poem will help you:

- discuss both the positive and negative affects of "labeling" people
- focus on images and diction
- share and compare interpretations
- write an imaginative memoir

Autumn Cycling Rob Gonsalves © 1995

They didn't know labels like ADD* back then.

For three days in Grade 8
I was popular, wasn't called Foster-4-eyes, Professor, Foss.
For three days
I had the other kids
fascinated at recess
by my imagination of a flying bicycle.

I told them how I
could make hydrogen and pump it into the wings
and soar off the end of Tutor Road,
cross the shore of Cadboro Bay and
land at Frank Hobbs School,
but I couldn't make it work out, no one listened
anymore, and I thought I couldn't do anything.

I had to get older, a lot older
to know Leonardo da Vinci drew books and
books of machines he never made
and some of them might have flown.

These days I still dream a lot
in the details of what might happen
and some dreams become words
and some words make themselves come true.

Activities

1. As a class, discuss the following questions:
   • Consider the following "names" (or labels): ADD, Foster-4-eyes, Professor, Foss. Which do you think are positive and which are negative? Why? How do labels affect both the people who are labeled and the people who use the label to describe someone else?
   • Reread the last stanza to reflect on its meaning. What do you think the poet means by "some dreams become words and some words make themselves come true."?

2. Based on the message of this poem, write a paragraph about someone you either know or have heard about who has turned a disability into an asset.

3. Research a learning disability. Then, imagine you are a person with this disability. As this person, write a memoir that focuses positively on some of the special skills or talents you have.

Canoe Manned by Voyageurs Passing a Waterfall
Frances Anne Hopkins

Hopkins, Frances Anne/National Archives of Canada/C-002771

Activities

1. Imagine that you are one of the voyageurs travelling through the Great Lakes. Write a diary entry for the day in 1869 shown in this painting.

2. This painting was created by Frances Anne Hopkins, the wife of a Hudson's Bay Company inspector. Hopkins often travelled by canoe through the Great Lakes. Closely examine the painting and the artist's technique. In groups, discuss how Hopkins captured this mode of travel.

Higher Ground   BEVERLEY BRENNA

Focus Your Learning
Reading this short story
will help you:
- share previous
  knowledge to further
  your understanding
  of the text
- use an organizer to
  understand the
  structure of the plot
- examine the theme of
  the story
- create a poster with a
  message derived
  from the story

Nellie Mooney dropped her basket of eggs and
picked up a stick to chase the speckled chicken to
the other side of the tidy, log henhouse. Her usually laughing
eyes were wide with anger. "Stay over there, you bad thing,"
she yelled, "or I'll put you in the stew pot. Stew pot!"

She turned and examined the yellow hen the other chicken
had been pecking. It fixed a watery eye on her as she clicked her
teeth at its bald and bleeding rump. Then it bobbed over to
where she had dropped her basket.

Nellie checked through the eggs. Two had been cracked by
the fall. Eggs were very dear, ten cents a dozen. Her first impulse
was to hide the broken ones under the straw, but she wanted her
mother to see what that awful chicken had made her do.

"Stew pot!" she hissed at it again. "I should let you out for the weasels." But she didn't. She carefully closed the henhouse door and headed up the hill to the farmhouse where she lived with her parents and five older siblings.

Her mother, however, did not lay the blame for the broken eggs on the chicken.

"Get the churn," said Mrs. Mooney crossly. "You will make the butter."

"But I—" Nellie began.

"Enough," warned her mother. "Do as you're told."

Inwardly, Nellie groaned. She had hoped to spend the morning outside collecting arrowheads among the goldenrod and piles of buffalo bones down by the creek. The buffalo had vanished in 1879, the year before Nellie's family had come to Manitoba. Secretly, Nellie hoped she'd see one of the lost giants after all, maybe among the poplar bluffs or galloping its way northwest across the prairie towards the mysterious, blue-black Brandon Hills.

Pushing the handle of the big, wooden churn made her arms ache and as the butter started to form, the foot pedal got harder and harder to press. As she worked, she thought of the First of July picnic in Millford that afternoon, wondering if there'd be chocolates. Someone had brought some to last year's picnic—the first Nellie had tasted—and she had made hers last as long as she could, enjoying the unbelievable sweetness.

Dreaming of the picnic, Nellie missed the rattle of the small chunks of new butter. Gas building up inside the churn popped the cork and cream flew everywhere.

"Oh Nellie, you didn't let it air!" cried her mother, running in to see rivulets of cream seeping into the cracks of the floor.

"It came too fast," Nellie exploded, much as the cream had done. "Stupid old stuff! I don't know why we need butter anyway—"

"You will learn to hold your tongue, young lady," interrupted her mother. "That is a lesson you seem reluctant to learn, but maybe

This well-known photograph of Nellie Mooney was taken after she had married Wes McClung. It depicts Nellie McClung at the height of her career as an author. She published sixteen books and countless stories and articles.

cleaning up this mess will teach you once and for all. Unless perhaps you'd prefer not to go to the picnic."

Nellie's arms and legs ached, but she went out and got the bucket and filled it with hot water from the stove.

"Hold your tongue, hold your tongue," she thought. "Someone's always telling me that."

As she scrubbed the floor, she recalled the discussion about politics her mother and brother had had the other day. Her brother hoped a young lawyer from Winnipeg would earn a seat in the local legislature, but her mother strongly disagreed with his choice.

"Just vote for who you like," Nellie had said to her mother to calm things down.

"Hush!" her mother snapped. "Women aren't allowed to vote."

"Not allowed to vote!" exclaimed Nellie. "But that's wrong!"

"Hold your tongue," said her mother.

"I'd like to throw this butter out the window," Nellie muttered when she had finished cleaning the floor. Then she smiled in spite of herself. "But first I'd like to churn that chicken into it."

Nellie tipped the heavy churn from side to side until the butter had chunked into one large piece. Then, her thin arms trembling, she carefully drained out the buttermilk and scooped the butter into a wooden bowl where she worked in the salt. Finally, the butter neatly squared inside paper wrappers, Nellie approached her mother.

"Isn't it almost time for the picnic?" she asked carefully.

"Yes, yes, I suppose it is," answered her mother. "Change into your church dress, with the straw hat to match. Your sisters are upstairs."

Nellie looked admiringly at the new print dress she pulled from the closet. Her mother had made it from material she brought from Ontario when they moved three years ago and Nellie was seven. The hat that went with the dress was lined with the same flowered cloth.

As Nellie climbed into the wagon behind her father, she noticed that her brothers hadn't had to change their clothes. Lizzie, one of Nellie's older sisters, carried the carrot gelatins their mother had set overnight in the cellar. Hannah, the other sister, carried cinnamon rolls, curled like snail shells. Their mother held the hamper which contained ham sandwiches, plates, cups, and cutlery, with two pies on top. Without fruit or eggs for the pies, Letitia Mooney had concocted a filling of molasses and butter thickened with bread crumbs and flavoured with vinegar and cinnamon. The three boys didn't carry anything.

Tables had been placed under the poplar trees by the flax blue water of the Souris River. When the Mooney family arrived, they added their contribution to what was already there. Nellie walked along, admiring the variety. On one table were placed devilled eggs, buns, slices of cheese, sandwiches, and hard boiled eggs. There were also plates of fried chicken—although not Old Stew Pot, thought Nellie regretfully. The next table held potato salads, cabbage salads, jellied salads, lettuce cut up in sour cream, and pickles. Then there were the pies, the doughnuts, the jelly rolls, the cookies. Large coffee urns stood over to one side, the smell of the brew better than the taste, thought Nellie. And there was lemonade in big, metal cream cans.

At a booth set up that morning and run by the district's welcoming committee, there was fresh ice cream made by Hettie Smith who had ice from winter kept in sawdust in an ice shack behind the house. Nellie had never tasted ice cream and she went over to take a peek. It looked like custard. The money made at this booth would go to welcome the new pioneers who had settled in the area, buying them baskets of supplies from the store in Millford. The smell of vanilla made Nellie's mouth water.

"Five cents a bowl," said one of the women running the booth.

Five cents! Nellie swallowed hard and thought of those broken eggs. She couldn't ask her mother for money now.

Instead, she got a plate and helped herself to the food on the tables. She didn't take any of her mother's sandwiches—they ate lots of ham at home—but filled her plate with fried chicken and a spoonful of each of the salads.

"Leave some for me!" called Jack, her next eldest brother.

Nellie saw from his plate that he was already returning for seconds.

"Pig!" she said.

While everyone ate, a brass band from Brandon played, with earth-shaking tones, "Rule Britannia," "The Maple Leaf," and "God Save the Queen," as well as other songs Nellie didn't recognize. After a baseball game which pitted married men against single men, the foot races began. Nellie's fists clenched in anticipation. The winners won a nickel—enough for ice cream! She hoped there would be a foot race for girls or at least one for girls and boys together.

Her mother frowned when she mentioned it.

"Girls, racing? Certainly not. Your skirts would fly up and your legs might show."

"But the boys show their—"

"Keep silent!" said her mother.

"Keep silent!" the politician cried, looking severely at an older Nellie where she stood at the front of the auditorium with the men. She was allowed to listen to politics but not, apparently, able to speak her mind.

Why were women only entitled to listen, staying at the back of the room like a herd of cattle? And why, when the elections came, were they not allowed to vote? Nellie pondered these questions as she listened to the rest of the politician's speech. But she didn't interrupt again. At least, not this time.

Nellie went off behind a poplar bluff and practised keeping her skirts down as she ran among the orange lilies. It was a hard thing to do. Her dress kept wrapping itself around her legs and with the thick red drawers underneath, she felt like a tethered pony. Disgusted, she plucked at some Saskatoon berries but they weren't yet ripe and left a dusty taste in her mouth.

Soon, everyone gathered for the slow-ox race. Nellie crossed her fingers for her father's black-and-white Jake. He was a gentle little ox and so pokey that at home they harnessed him to another ox to get him going. This time though, the slowest ox of all won the prize and the prize was a big box of raisins from Read and Callendar's store.

As was the custom, owners didn't ride their own oxen. A neighbour's hired man—Jimmy Sloan—rode Jake, trying to get him to move as fast as possible by waving his straw hat and howling like a coyote. Jake, true to himself, twitched his ears and would not be hurried.

Nellie pushed Mrs. Dale's baby buggy along the hill at the side of the race, proud that Mrs. Dale was counting on her to look after baby Sara.

"Who can I count on?"

Nellie looked around at the other quilters. They were all ignoring the plea from the minister's wife to sign a petition to Parliament requesting a vote for Canadian women.

"I'll sign," Nellie said.

There were a few audible gasps from the other women. Nellie Mooney, the teacher, was going to sign the petition.

"Women should help each other," Nellie said quietly as she signed her name.

"Got a smile?" Nellie tickled baby Sara under the chin and then pushed the buggy up onto higher ground.

Suddenly, black-and-white Jake leaped forward. Jimmy Sloan was thrown sideways, sending a whisky bottle flying out of his jacket, and the ox lurched up the rise to where Nellie stood with the baby. Nellie saw him coming but she didn't run. Jake crashed past, inches away, his eyes white, his sides squeezing like a bellows. Nellie saw Jake's stomach painted with blood. Jimmy Sloan had cheated and used spurs! He got up unsteadily and started away. He was drunk.

Hot anger washed over Nellie.

"You—you—you should be *ashamed* of yourself!" she cried, the words cool on her tongue. "You should—"

"And what about you, Mrs. Nellie McClung? Who's darning your husband's socks while you're out making your speeches?" sneered a man from the audience.

"A woman's place is in the home, with her children!" called another man angrily.

"I dare say her husband's dead," muttered a woman.

Nellie looked calmly across the hall. When she continued speaking, her voice was pleasant.

"My family is well, thank you, they'll be glad you asked after them. My husband did have a slight cold last year, but he is quite recovered. And," she lowered her voice in a conspiratorial whisper, "his socks are in excellent shape — he will be delighted at your concern."

Laughter rippled across the room.

"But I must ask you," Nellie went on, her voice increasing in force, "Would it be right to shut the door of the church in the faces of half the congregation? Is it wise to close the shop at noon, turning away half the day's customers? Half of this town is women, am I not correct? When you look into the eyes of your mother, your wife, your sister...are you not ashamed to tell them that when they travel, the only accident insurance available is for men? Why is this? And why, when your daughters may join you at church or at the store, are they turned away at the voters' box?" Nellie looked into the eyes of her listeners. "Those of you who stand in the way of half this town should be, and I'll say it again, ashamed."

"Ashamed!" Nellie called after Jimmy Sloan's retreating figure.

"Hush, Nellie," said her mother, coming up the hill to take her arm.

"No, I won't hush! He hurt our Jake and he could have hurt me. And the baby!" She stood dizzily and looked down the hill at the man who was still weaving away from the crowd.

"You should—you should—you're just a real COWARD, Mr. Sloan! A REAL COWARD!" she yelled. The more she spoke, the lighter she felt, until it seemed her feet weren't touching the ground at all. "COWARD!" A white-faced Mrs. Dale gathered baby Sara in her arms, choking back sobs.

Mrs. Mooney pushed the baby buggy down the hill, leading Nellie, stiff-legged, along with it. Her mother didn't look at her when she said quietly, "You stood your ground and saved the baby, Nellie. Good girl."

"I'll stand my ground on this," said Nellie to the Premier of Manitoba.

"Take it from me, Mrs. McClung," he told her. "Nice women don't want the vote."

"Maybe your nice women aren't working in dirty factories. They're not widows begging money from their sons, and they're not watching their children go hungry while their drunken husbands do what they please," snapped Nellie. "I know many nice women in these situations and, believe me, they want to pick Members of Parliament who will make laws to help them."

The Premier didn't respond. He was thinking about what this woman was saying and wondering uncomfortably if perhaps it mightn't be better to have her on his side after all.

At the bottom of the hill, Mrs. Dale nodded at Nellie, her eyes still full of tears.

"Thank you," she said.

Nellie held her pride like a chocolate in her cheek. For once that day, she had done the right thing.

Activities

1. As a class, discuss what you know about Nellie McClung. What did she contribute to Canadian history?

2. To understand better how the incidents in this story are connected, make an organizer. Use two categories, "Childhood Incident" and "Adult Incident," and find four examples for each. Each childhood incident is related to an adult incident; be sure to place related incidents next to each other. At what point did you realize that this story was about Nellie McClung? What effect did this realization have on you?

3. Even as a child, Nellie dared speak out about what she thought were injustices. What would you do if you witnessed instances of bullying, racism, harassment, or discrimination at your school? Work in a small group to discuss possible responses to one of these problems. Then create a poster with a message based on your conclusions.

The Ukrainian Pioneer #3 William Kurelek

National Gallery of Canada, Ottawa; Transfer from the House of Commons of the Parliament of Canada, 1990; Courtesy, the Estate of William Kurelek and The Isaacs Gallery.

Activities

1. Settlers in Canada had to clear their own land. The man in this
   picture is showing his family the path he must clear. What do you
   think he is saying to his wife and children? Write the monologue to
   go with this visual.

2. This picture was created on wood. Explain why the use of this
   medium is ironic. How do the medium and the techniques in the
   picture combine to send a message?

Things Past
DORA FORSTROM

The North Woods, 1976 Dora Forstrom

Focus Your Learning
Reading this memoir will help you:
- think about the way we remember
- write a poem that summarizes the main ideas of the text
- experiment with language

When my father left Pajala, a small Swedish village above the Arctic Circle, for Canada, he travelled a well-trodden route: he followed his sister to a place of similar landscape, climate, and industry to "the old country" which was suddenly of his past. Canada had the wind, cold, rocks, lakes, fir trees, and lumber industry of home. Here, he joined a community of immigrants who shared his language, his skills, and the transplanted camaraderie of a place that, as a child, seemed too distant and inaccessible for me ever to visit. In fact, it was not until I was married with young children of my own that I "walked backwards" along my father's footsteps to a place where the lilting foreign sounds of my first language came back to me.

My mother's parents came to Canada from Sweden's capital city of Stockholm in 1902. She was born in Norman, an enclave of mostly Swedish immigrants on the outskirts of the town of Rat Portage in northwestern Ontario. The odd name of the town was derived from a natural event. This spot was where the muskrats "portaged" between the Winnipeg River and Lake of the Woods. This lake of my childhood, a magnificent body of water projecting down into the state of Minnesota, is speckled with eight thousand islands. It is a place where we would try to waterski from island to island by holding a rope attached to a pontoon plane that never left the surface of the water. This effort was, I suppose, a human portage of sorts.

Around the time my parents met, the people of Rat Portage decided to have a contest to create a new, more attractive name for the town. So they took the "KE"

from the neighbouring town of Keewatin, the "NO" from Norman, and the "RA" from Rat Portage—and I was born in Kenora in 1922.

There was no kindergarten in those days. When I was age five and my cousin and daily playmate Doug turned six, I walked him to his first day of school. When we arrived, I sat cross-legged in the middle of the floor and told the teacher, Miss Rolanson, that I wouldn't get up until she agreed to let me stay. So it turned out to be my first day of school as well.

We adored Miss Rolanson. Every morning we'd go to meet her on her way to school by waiting for her at the stile. A stile was a set of steps that went up one side of a fence and down the other so you could get across. The postmistress Nellie Patterson also crossed the stile each day. She would carry the bag of outgoing mail and hang it on a post near the train tracks. The train would stop, take that bag, and put the bag of ingoing mail in its place.

Sometimes the bag would hold a letter for my father from my "farmor," meaning my father's mother. On the day he left Pajala, his mother lit a candle in the window, which she said she would light every night until he returned. She did light it every single night. But in those days, travel was very difficult and expensive. They never saw each other again.

At school, we used to have "health

inspection." That meant that we had to report to Miss Rolanson whether we had had a bath and brushed our teeth. She would then inspect our fingernails and teeth to see if we were telling the truth. When she told me I had teeth like pearls, I was very perplexed, because no matter how long I gazed in a mirror, they never seemed round to me. It did not occur to me to challenge her description.

After school, my mormor, meaning my mother's mother, would milk her cow, named Bossy. As mormor positioned herself on a little stool and got to work, I would hold Bossy's tail. That way Bossy wouldn't slap mormor when she swished her tail to chase away the flies.

Mormor would take the milk, which was still warm from the cow, and thicken it to make "chockmyulk," Swedish for "thick milk." But the favourite drink of adults was coffee. My Uncle John would quietly take his coffee. That's in part because, when he left Sweden, he forgot much of the Swedish language. Unfortunately, he also never learned English.

Tunnel Island, 1946 Dora Forstrom

If the coffee was too hot, my morfar, my mother's father, would pour some into his saucer and drink it from there. I was fascinated to watch him put two lumps of sugar between his front teeth and sip his coffee through the sugar lumps. Sometimes he'd dip a sugar lump in his coffee and then give it to me. He would tell me how, in the old country, if a man wanted to marry a woman, he would go to her family's home, and there, he would say to her parents, "I'd like a cup of coffee." That meant he wanted to marry their daughter. If they said that they had no coffee, he had not been accepted as a son-in-law. I guess that had something to do with coffee being the adults' favourite drink.

And so at the age of seventy-six, I sit here in my condominium, travelling the footprints of memory as I sip on my dark cup of coffee.

Activities

1. The coffee serves as a reminder to Dora Forstrom, bringing back memories of her childhood. Often certain sights, smells, or sounds will trigger memories. Talk to a partner about a memory of yours that has been triggered in this way. What does this tell you about the way in which the brain recalls memories? How might this memory trigger-effect help you study and remember?

2. Use words and images from the narrative to create a found poem that summarizes the main ideas of this memory piece.

3. Work with a partner to review the words that the author has to explain. In your own words, explain how some of these words were created. What did they blend? With your partner, create your own set of words that blend together commonly known words. Pick a set of objects (e.g., things in your bedroom or classroom) and rename them using the same techniques as the Swedish Canadians. Create a mini-dictionary of these new words. You might choose to present some of the words to your classmates and see if they can guess their meaning.

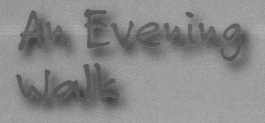

An Evening Walk

Emma LaRocque

Focus Your Learning
Reading this poem will help you:
- understand the motives of a character
- identify the literary device of alliteration
- comprehend the theme of the poem

The rush sound of a distant waterfall,

a furtive rustling of leaves and cones

whispering their dusky tales

called to me

to alloy

the tracks, sand and rocks

with my city shoes.

There are some walks

one must take alone.

Pemmican Land Jane Ash Poitras

But then

I heard a double squeal
and looked to see a little boy
with his "doggie"—
I called them away.

There are some walks
one must take alone.

But then

two sets of stooped shoulders
sniffed the sandy backroad
back to Kokums.
I thought of my need to be alone,
looked at my rocks and steel and
sand

But then

I ran after the stoop of shoulders
I gave him my hand—
to my unmerited surprise
he held out his,
and in the other
he held a bunch of clumpish clovers

and said:
"Smell my trees, Aunty."

There is something to
an evening walk
hand in hand
with a brown boy with clovers
he has to hold above his head
because his uncontainable puppy
likes them too.
Ne-me-you-bi-moo-tan-nan.

Activities

1. Explain why you think the author changed her mind about walking alone.

2. Identify three examples of alliteration in this poem. With a partner, read the lines aloud. What effect does each example create?

3. In the last line, the author speaks to the little boy in their Aboriginal language. What do you imagine she is saying? Write a concluding line in English that you think would be appropriate for this poem.

À l'île blanche

(At White Island)

Acadian Folksong

At White Island where we safely

Dropped anchor,

The captain got everyone to listen

And he began to give orders:

"Let us have the courage to raise anchor,

Alas! we have to set sail."

Alas! I sailed in the open sea

Until eleven o'clock next morning,

I saw a great big ship coming,

It was certainly a warship.

Coming closer, we prepared to give chase:

"We shall attack it from the rear."

We attacked this great big ship from the rear,

And fired three cannon shots.

It was to let them know

That we were ready for them.

In preparation for the battle,

I brought ninety cannons to bear.

"Bring along your launch boat, oh!

Bring along your launch boat, oh God!"

I'm at last aware that the beautiful frigate

Had at last seen reason.

Focus Your Learning
Reading these song lyrics will help you:
- focus on the characteristics of legends and folksongs
- explain the purpose of folksongs
- write a moral based on the message of the song

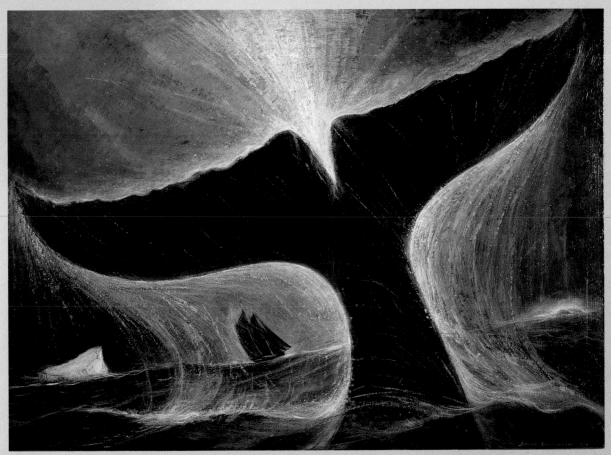

In the Labrador Sea David Blackwood

Activities

1. Many legends and folksongs describe confrontations between a powerful opponent and a small but brave protagonist. In point form, and with specific references from the song, explain how "À l'île blanche" fits this format. What do you think is the purpose of folksongs of this sort?

2. Write a moral or short saying explaining a lesson that could be learned from the story told in this song.

When I Was a Little Girl

Joy Kogawa

When I was a little girl
We used to walk together
Tim, my brother who wore glasses,
And I, holding hands
Tightly as we crossed the bridge
And he'd murmur, "You pray now"
—being a clergyman's son—
Until the big white boys
Had kicked on past.
Later we'd climb the bluffs
Overhanging the ghost town
And pick the small white lilies
And fling them like bombers
Over Slocan.

Focus Your Learning

Reading this poem will help you:
- create an illustration or collage based on the text
- construct meaning from the text
- role-play a scene responding to the text

PINE CRESCENT SCHOOL

A school photograph taken during the time Joy Kogawa spent in the internment camp at Slocan City. She is sitting in the front row, on the far right. The writer and broadcaster David Suzuki is standing in the back row, on the far left.

Activities

1. Draw two illustrations for this poem or create a two-panel collage showing, first, the children crossing the bridge and, then, the children "bombing" the town. Be sure to include the key images as described in the poem.

2. What is the poet saying about the human need for revenge? Write a short-answer response, defending your view with details from the poem.

3. Work in a small group to create a scene that shows an effective strategy to deal with racism or with being bullied. Role-play your scene for the class.

The Stolen Party

LILIANA HEKER

Focus Your Learning
Reading this story will help you:
- role-play characters to understand their motivation
- examine how point of view can change interpretation of events
- develop your interpretation of the story's ending

As soon as she arrived she went straight to the kitchen to see if the monkey was there.

It was: what a relief! She wouldn't have liked to admit that her mother had been right. *Monkeys at a birthday?* her mother had sneered. *Get away with you, believing any nonsense you're told!* She was cross, but not because of the monkey, the girl thought: it's just because of the party.

"I don't like you going," she told her. "It's a rich people's party."

"Rich people go to Heaven too," said the girl, who studied religion at school. She was barely nine, and one of the best in her class.

"I'm going because I've been invited," she said. "And I've been invited because Luciana is my friend. So there."

"Ah yes, your friend," her mother grumbled. She paused. "Listen, Rosaura," she said at last. "That one's not your friend. You know what you are to them? The maid's daughter, that's what."

Rosaura blinked hard: she wasn't going to cry. Then she yelled: "Shut up! You know nothing about being friends!"

Every afternoon she used to go to Luciana's house and they would both finish their homework while Rosaura's mother did the cleaning.

They had their tea in the kitchen and they told each other secrets. Rosaura loved everything in the big house, and she also loved the people who lived there.

"I'm going because it will be the most lovely party in the whole world, Luciana told me it would. There will be a magician, and he will bring a monkey and everything."

The mother swung around to take a good look at her child, and pompously put her hands on her hips.

"Monkeys at a birthday?" she said. "Get away with you, believing any nonsense you're told!"

Rosaura was deeply offended. She thought it unfair of her mother to accuse other people of being liars simply because they were rich. Rosaura too wanted to be rich, of course. If one day she managed to live in a beautiful palace, would her mother stop loving her? She felt very sad. She wanted to go to that party more than anything else in the world.

"I'll die if I don't go," she whispered, almost without moving her lips. And she wasn't sure whether she had been heard, but on the morning of the party she discovered that her mother had starched her Christmas dress. And in the afternoon, after washing her hair, her mother rinsed it in apple vinegar so that it would be all nice and shiny. Before going out, Rosaura admired herself in the mirror, with her white dress and glossy hair, and thought she looked terribly pretty.

Señora Ines also seemed to notice. As soon as she saw her, she said: "How lovely you look today, Rosaura."

Rosaura gave her starched skirt a slight toss with her hands and walked into the party with a firm step. She said hello to Luciana and asked about the monkey. Luciana put on a secretive look and whispered into Rosaura's ear: "He's in the kitchen. But don't tell anyone, because it's a surprise."

Rosaura wanted to make sure. Carefully she entered the kitchen and there she saw it: deep in thought, inside its cage. It looked so funny that the girl stood there for a while, watching it, and later, every so often, she would slip out of the party unseen and go and admire it. Rosaura was the only one allowed into the kitchen. Señora Ines had said, "You yes, but not the others, they're much too boisterous, they might break something." Rosaura had never broken anything. She even managed the jug of orange juice, carrying it from the kitchen into the dining-room. She held it carefully and didn't spill a single drop. And Señora Ines had said: "Are you sure you can manage a jug as big as that?" Of course she could manage. She wasn't a butterfingers, like the others. Like that blonde girl with the bow in her hair. As soon as she saw Rosaura, the girl with the bow had said:

"And you? Who are you?"

"I'm a friend of Luciana," said Rosaura.

"No," said the girl with the bow, "you are not a friend of Luciana because I'm her cousin and I know all her friends. And I don't know you."

"So what," said Rosaura. "I come here every afternoon with my mother and we do our homework together."

"You and your mother do your homework together?" asked the girl, laughing.

"I and Luciana do our homework together," said Rosaura, very seriously.

The girl with the bow shrugged her shoulders.

"That's not being friends," she said. "Do you go to school together?"

"No."

"So where do you know her from?" said the girl, getting impatient.

Rosaura remembered her mother's words perfectly. She took a deep breath.

"I'm the daughter of the employee," she said.

Her mother had said very clearly: "If someone asks, you say you're the daughter of the employee; that's all." She also told her to add: "And proud of it." But Rosaura thought that never in her life would she dare say something of the sort.

"What employee?" said the girl with the bow. "Employee in a shop?"

"No," said Rosaura angrily. "My mother doesn't sell anything in any shop, so there."

"So how come she's an employee?" said the girl with the bow. Just then Señora Ines arrived saying *shh shh,* and asked Rosaura if she wouldn't mind helping serve out the hot-dogs, as she knew the house so much better than the others.

"See?" said Rosaura to the girl with the bow, and when no one was looking she kicked her in the shin.

Apart from the girl with the bow, all the others were delightful. The one she liked best was Luciana, with her golden birthday crown; and then the boys. Rosaura won the sack race, and nobody managed to catch her when they played tag. When they split into two teams to play charades, all the boys wanted her for their side. Rosaura felt she had never been so happy in all her life.

But the best was still to come. The best came after Luciana blew out the candles. First the cake. Señora Ines had asked her to help pass the cake around, and Rosaura had enjoyed the task immensely, because everyone called out to her, shouting "Me, me!" Rosaura remembered a story in which there was a queen who had the power of life or death over her subjects. She had always loved that, having the power of life or death. To Luciana and the boys she gave the largest pieces, and to the girl with the bow she gave a slice so thin one could see through it.

After the cake came the magician, tall and bony, with a fine red cape. A true magician: he could untie handkerchiefs by blowing on them and make a chain with links that had no openings. He could guess what cards were pulled out from a pack, and the monkey was his assistant. He called the monkey "partner." "Let's see here, partner," he would say, "turn over a card." And, "Don't run away, partner; time to work now."

The final trick was wonderful. One of the children had to hold the monkey in his arms and the magician said he would make him disappear.

"What, the boy?" they all shouted.

"No, the monkey!" shouted back the magician.

Rosaura thought that this was truly the most amusing party in the whole world.

The magician asked a small fat boy to come and help, but the small fat boy got frightened almost at once and dropped the monkey on the floor. The magician picked him up carefully, whispered something in his ear, and the monkey nodded almost as if he understood.

"You mustn't be so unmanly, my friend," the magician said to the fat boy.

"What's unmanly?" said the fat boy.

The magician turned around as if to look for spies.

"A sissy," said the magician. "Go sit down."

Then he stared at all the faces, one by one. Rosaura felt her heart tremble.

"You, with the Spanish eyes," said the magician. And everyone saw that he was pointing at her.

She wasn't afraid. Neither holding the monkey, nor when the magician made him vanish; not even when, at the end, the magician flung his red cape over Rosaura's head and uttered a few magic words ... and the monkey reappeared, chattering happily, in her arms. The children clapped furiously. And before Rosaura returned to her seat, the magician said:

"Thank you very much, my little countess."

She was so pleased with the compliment that a while later, when her mother came to fetch her, that was the first thing she told her.

"I helped the magician and he said to me, 'Thank you very much, my little countess.'"

It was strange because up to then Rosaura had thought that she was angry with her mother. All along Rosaura had imagined that she would say to her: "See that the monkey wasn't a lie?" But instead she was so thrilled that she told her mother all about the wonderful magician.

Her mother tapped her on the head and said: "So now we're a countess!"

But one could see that she was beaming.

And now they both stood in the entrance, because a moment ago Señora Ines, smiling, had said: "Please wait here a second."

Her mother suddenly seemed worried.

"What is it?" she asked Rosaura.

"What is what?" said Rosaura. "It's nothing; she just wants to get the presents for those who are leaving, see?"

She pointed at the fat boy and at a girl with pigtails who were also waiting there, next to their mothers. And she explained about the presents. She knew, because she had been watching those who left before her. When one of the girls was about to leave, Señora Ines would give her a bracelet. When a boy left, Señora Ines gave him a yo-yo. Rosaura preferred the yo-yo because it sparkled, but she didn't mention that to her mother. Her mother might have said: "So why don't you ask for one, you blockhead?" That's what her mother was like. Rosaura didn't feel like explaining that she'd be horribly ashamed to be the odd one out. Instead she said:

"I was the best-behaved at the party."

And she said no more because Señora Ines came out into the hall with two bags, one pink and one blue.

First she went up to the fat boy, gave him a yo-yo out of the blue bag, and the fat boy left with his mother. Then she went up to the girl and gave her a bracelet out of the pink bag, and the girl with the pigtails left as well.

Finally she came up to Rosaura and her mother. She had a big smile on her face and Rosaura liked that. Señora Ines looked down at her, then looked up at her mother, and then said something that made Rosaura proud:

"What a marvellous daughter you have, Herminia."

For an instant, Rosaura thought that she'd give her two presents: the bracelet and the yo-yo. Señora Ines bent down as if about to look for something. Rosaura also leaned forward, stretching out her arm. But she never completed the movement.

Señora Ines didn't look in the pink bag. Nor did she look in the blue bag. Instead she rummaged in her purse. In her hand appeared two bills.

"You really and truly earned this," she said handing them over. "Thank you for all your help, my pet."

Rosaura felt her arms stiffen, stick close to her body, and then she noticed her mother's hand on her shoulder. Instinctively she pressed herself against her mother's body. That was all. Except her eyes. Rosaura's eyes had a cold, clear look that fixed itself on Señora Ines's face.

Señora Ines, motionless, stood there with her hand outstretched. As if she didn't dare draw it back. As if the slightest change might shatter an infinitely delicate balance.

Activities

1. What happened before this story began? With a partner, prepare a role play in which Luciana asks her mother to allow Rosaura to be invited to the birthday party. What are Luciana's motives likely to be? How is her mother likely to respond? Present your role play to the class.

2. The way Rosaura sees herself at the party is quite different from the way others see her. Choose one other character from this story and retell events at the party from this character's point of view.

3. What happened after the conclusion to this story? Write Rosaura's diary entry, explaining what she has learned and how the party has affected her outlook on life.

While I Was Looking at the Background You Walked Out of the Picture

Jan Conn

I've sent you a tiger. Its fur burns intense orange,
radiant against the dark. Plants around it
send up volleys of smells, fantastic.

Its ears are filled with white hair,
a thousand moth antennae
bent in and listening to dreams
of the rain forest: fat frogs creaking,
a prey of insects crackling.

You leave me behind, always,
coming home months later, from India,
Africa, Colombia—with another
smell on your skin, a suitcase
of saris and ivory elephants for your wife,

and smaller gifts for us, the daughters, growing
like Hallowe'en pumpkins, awkward teeth
stuck in our grins.

I decide to become an archaeologist,
to go where you've been
while the scent is still fresh.

Activities

1. Assume the role of the poet as a child. Tell your father how you feel about his absences and what you would like to have happen.

2. Identify words or phrases in the poem that appeal to sight, sound, and smell. Then find a picture of a place that you have been or would like to visit. Paste the picture in the centre of a large piece of paper. Think about the sights, sounds, smells, and feelings that you associate with this place, and record words and phrases that give a vivid description. Use these words as the basis to write a poem.

1. Write a series of letters that might have been written between Irina Ratushinskaya and Nelson Mandela during their time in prison. They should share information about their respective causes and ideas about why it is important to fight for their causes even as they endure the hardships of prison life.

2. Make a collage that illustrates how the poems in this unit use the five senses to create memorable language. As well as pictures that portray sound, sight, touch, smell, and taste, you might also include key words that exemplify these sensory impressions.

3. Create a dialogue that portrays the opposing points of view of two characters you have met in this section. For example, the girl from "Black Patent Leather Shoes" might disagree with Rosaura about getting dressed up.

4. With a small group, create a panel discussion on female gender roles in our society. How is it that little girls learn their gender roles? How does this differ from the gender roles expected of them in earlier times? Support your arguments with examples taken from selections in this unit as well as from everyday life.

5. Create a mobile for the classroom that depicts your ideas on what a hero should be. Use pictures and words in your mobile, drawing as much as possible on the selections in this section.

6. Take any one prose passage or selection in this unit, and turn it into a poem. To do this, take out all unnecessary words, leaving only the strongest, or select a handful of the strongest terms. Concentrate on creating a concise form to express your ideas, and on using poetic devices such as simile, alliteration, onomatopoeia, etc.

7. Review all the journal entries that you have written for activities in this unit. Take your favourite piece and revise it in any format, transforming it into a memorable piece of writing.

8. Look back through the selections and find a topic about which you would like to know more. With your teacher, design a research project on that topic. Choose a form for reporting on your research, and decide on the criteria you will need to meet.

9. Make a portfolio of all the work you have done for this section of the anthology. Clearly mark original pieces and those that have been revised. Write a short assessment of your work, outlining your strengths and areas that need improvement. Determine areas for future learning focus, and strategies for success.

4 look beyond

What happens when you focus on the future? How much of it is blurry? And what parts—if any—are crystal clear?

Polish your viewfinder as you consider how to predict the future...and how to create it.

The Earth-ling

Brian Patten

Countless years ago the people of Alzorus used the planet Earth as a lunatic asylum. They called the people they dumped there "Earth-lings."

I am an earth-ling.
My memory goes back a long way.
I was dumped here long ago.
I lived beneath some overhanging rocks.
Around me at night, through the sky's black sheet,
stars poured down.
It was lonely sitting for centuries
beneath that rain-drenched rock,
wrapped in furs, afraid of this whole terrible planet.
I grew fed up with the taste of its food.
I made fire, I slaughtered creatures,
I walked through a forest and made friends.
I copied the things they made.
I walked through another forest and found enemies,
I destroyed the things they made.
I went on and on and on and on,
and on a bit more.
I crossed mountains, I crossed new oceans.
I became familiar with this world.
Time would not stop running when I asked it.
I could not whistle for it to come back.
I invented a couple of languages.
I wrote things down.
I invented books.
Time passed.
My inventions piled up. The natives of this planet
feared me.
Some tried to destroy me.
Rats came. A great plague swept over the world.
Many of me died.
I am an earth-ling.
I invented cities. I tore them down.
I sat in comfort. I sat in poverty. I sat in boredom.

Home was a planet called Alzorus. A tiny far off star—
One night it went out. It vanished.
I am an earth-ling, exiled for ever from my beginnings.
Time passed. I did things. Time passed. I grew exhausted.
One day
A great fire swept the world.
I wanted to go back to the beginning.
It was impossible.
The rock I had squatted under melted.
Friends became dust,
Dust became the only friend.
In the dust I drew faces of people.
I am putting this message on a feather
and puffing it up among the stars.
I have missed so many things out!
But this is the basic story, the terrible story.
I am an earth-ling,
I was dumped here long ago.
Mistakes were made.

Activities

1. In a small group, practise a choral reading of the poem. Consider adding sound effects. Practise stresses and pauses for effect. Present the choral reading to the class. Discuss how each group's reading was similar and different. How do the differences affect the way you envision the poem or the narrator?

2. The narrator says that he "missed so many things out." Work with a partner to create a set of lines to explain what he missed out. Look at the form of the poem, especially the use of repetition, and try to emulate it in your new lines.

From Glenn to Glenn   Adapted from *Time* Magazine

APR. 13, 1970
Moon mission cut short because oxygen tank ruptures, after which crew returns safely to Earth

JULY 20, 1969
U.S. astronauts Neil Armstrong and Buzz Aldrin walk on moon

DEC. 21, 1968
First manned mission to orbit moon is launched from Florida

JAN. 27, 1967
Flash fire in Apollo 1 on launch pad in Florida kills 3 astronauts

FEB. 20, 1962
Astronaut John Glenn becomes first American to orbit Earth

MAY 25, 1961
U.S. President Kennedy vows men will go to moon by end of decade

MAY 5, 1961
First American in space

APR. 12, 1961
Soviet cosmonaut is first person to orbit Earth

OCT. 4, 1957
Soviet Union launches first artificial satellite

DEC. 4-10, 1993
Astronauts capture Hubble Space Telescope and fully repair its optics

APR. 25, 1990
When astronauts on Discovery place Hubble Space Telescope into Earth's orbit, they realize its mirror is wrong shape

FEB. 8, 1987
Russia launches first continuously inhabited space station

JAN. 28, 1986
Challenger explodes 73 seconds after take-off, killing all 7 people on board

JUNE 18, 1983
Astronaut Sally Ride becomes first American woman in space

APR. 12, 1981
First launch of reusable manned spacecraft Columbia

JULY 11, 1979
Unmanned Skylab crashes to Earth, scattering debris across Australia and Indian Ocean

MAR. 22, 1995
Russian Cosmonaut returns to Earth after spending a record 437 days in space

JUNE 29, 1995
U.S.'s 100th manned space mission Atlantis docks with Russian spacecraft Mir in space

Launch of Discovery on Oct. 29, 1998

JULY 4, 1997	OCT. 29, 1998
U.S. Sojourner rover lands on and explores Mars, where it falls silent 83 days later	77-year-old John Glenn launches into space a second time, aboard space shuttle Discovery

77-year-old astronaut John Glenn.

Focus Your Learning
Studying this time-line will help you:
- examine the structure and techniques used
- prepare a speech based on information in the text
- explain how pictorial features aid understanding of a text

Activities

1. This article compares space travel, past and present. What techniques does it use to help the reader understand the main historical events?

2. After researching on the Internet or CD-ROM encyclopedias, prepare a short speech telling about three historic events in the space program. Be sure to include an attention-getting opening sentence and a powerful conclusion.

3. By featuring astronaut John Glenn, the article puts a human face on the history of events. How does this help people relate to the NASA achievements and discoveries in science?

The Moth and the Star

JAMES THURBER

A young and impressionable moth once set his heart on a certain star. He told his mother about this and she counselled him to set his heart on a bridge lamp instead. "Stars aren't the thing to hang around," she said. "Lamps are the thing to hang around." "You get somewhere that way," said the moth's father, "You don't get anywhere chasing stars." But the moth would not heed the words of either parent. Every evening at dusk when the star came out he would start flying toward it and every morning at dawn he would crawl back home worn out with his vain endeavour. One day his father said to him, "You haven't burned a wing in months, boy, and it looks to me as if you were never going to. All your brothers have been badly burned flying around street lamps and all your sisters have been terribly singed flying around house lamps. Come on, now, get out of here and get yourself scorched! A big strapping moth like you without a mark on him!"

The moth left his father's house, but he would not fly around street lamps and he would not fly around house lamps. He went right on trying to reach the star, which was four-and-one-third light years, or twenty-five trillion miles, away. The moth thought it was just caught in the top branches of the elm. He never did reach the star, but he went right on trying, night after night, and when he was a very, very old moth he began to think that he really had reached the star and he went around saying so. This gave him a deep and lasting pleasure, and he lived to a great old age. His parents and his brothers and his sisters had all been burned to death when they were quite young.

MORAL: *Who flies afar from the sphere of our sorrow is here today and here tomorrow.*

Activities

1. The moth's dreams were different from those of his father and his siblings. Work with a partner to make a visual organizer that shows the differences. Create a second organizer to show how your dreams might be different from those of your parents.

2. Look carefully at the moral of the fable. Explain it in your own words. Share your explanation with the class. Paraphrase the fable to show how the fable demonstrates the moral.

3. Explain why the ending of this fable is ironic. In what ways might it have ended differently? Write a short paragraph giving the fable a different ending.

4. Write a fable of your own, with a moral. Start by developing the moral. Share the moral with a partner and help each other to develop unique story lines. Develop a rough draft of your fable and share it with another partner. Help each other to develop ideas and descriptive language. Share your second draft with a third partner and help each other to proofread for errors. Do a final copy. You might wish to develop your fable into a children's story book.

A Wish Named Arnold

CHARLES DE LINT

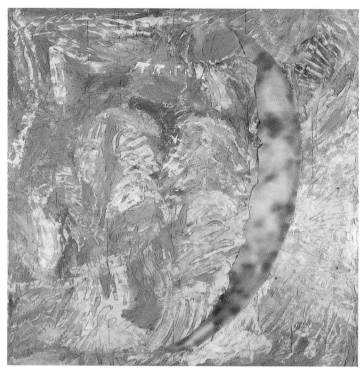

Decadent Crescent Moon © 1990 Paterson Ewen

Marguerite kept a wish in a brass egg and its name was Arnold.

The egg screwed apart in the middle. Inside, wrapped in a small piece of faded velvet, was the wish. It was a small wish, about the length of a man's thumb, and was made of black clay in the rough shape of a bird. Marguerite decided straight away that it was a crow, even if it did have a splash of white on its head. That made it just more special for her, because she'd dyed a forelock of her own dark hair a peroxide white just before the summer started—much to her parents' dismay.

She'd found the egg under a pile of junk in Miller's while tagging along with her mother and aunt on their usual weekend tour of the local antique shops. Miller's was near their cottage on Otty Lake, just down the road from Rideau Ferry, and considered to be the best antique shop in the area.

The egg and its dubious contents were only two dollars, and maybe the egg was dinged-up a little and didn't screw together quite right, and maybe the carving didn't look so much like a crow as it did a lump of black clay with what could be a beak on it, but she'd bought it all the same.

It wasn't until Arnold talked to her that she found out he was a wish.

"What do you mean you're a wish?" she'd asked, keeping her voice low so that her parents wouldn't think she'd taken to talking in her sleep. "Like a genie in a lamp?"

Something like that.

It was all quite confusing. Arnold lay in her hand, an unmoving lump that was definitely not alive even if he did look like a bird, sort of. That was a plain fact, as her father liked to say. On the other hand, someone was definitely speaking to her in a low buzzing voice that tickled pleasantly inside her head.

I wonder if I'm dreaming, she thought.

She gave her white forelock a tug, then brushed it away from her brow and bent down to give the clay bird a closer look.

"What sort of a wish can you give me?" she asked finally.

Think of something—any one thing that you want—and I'll give it to you.

"Anything?"

Within reasonable limits.

Marguerite nodded sagely. She was all too familiar with *that* expression. "Reasonable limits" was why she only had one forelock dyed instead of a whole swath of rainbow colours like her friend Tina, or a Mohawk like Sheila. If she just washed her hair and let it dry, *and* you ignored the dyed forelock, she had a most reasonable short haircut. But all it took was a little gel that she kept hidden in her purse and by the time she joined her friends at the mall, her hair was sticking out around her head in a bristle of spikes. It was just such a

Within reasonable limits

pain wearing a hat when she came home and having to wash out the gel right away.

Maybe that should be her wish. That she could go around looking just however she pleased and nobody could tell her any different. Except that seemed like a waste of a wish. She should probably ask for great heaps of money and jewels. Or maybe for a hundred more wishes.

"How come I only get one wish?" she asked.

Because that's all I am, Arnold replied. *One small wish.*

"Genies and magic fish give three. In fact *everybody* in *all* the stories usually gets three. Isn't it a tradition or something?"

Not where I come from.

"Where do you come from?"

There was a moment's pause, then Arnold said softly, *I'm not really sure.*

Marguerite felt a little uncomfortable at that. The voice tickling her mind sounded too sad and she started to feel ashamed of being so greedy.

"Listen," she said. "I didn't really mean to … you know …"

That's all right, Arnold replied. *Just let me know when you've decided what your wish is.*

Marguerite got a feeling in her head then, as though something had just slipped away, like a lost memory or a half-remembered thought, then she realized that Arnold had just gone back to wherever it was that he'd been before she'd opened the egg. Thoughtfully, she wrapped him up in the faded velvet, then shut him away in the egg. She put the egg under her pillow and went to sleep.

All the next day she kept thinking about the brass egg and the clay crow inside it, about her one wish and all the wonderful things that there were to wish for. She meant to take out the egg right away, first thing in the morning, but she never quite found the time. She went fishing with her father after breakfast, and then she went into Perth to shop with her mother, and then she went swimming with Steve who lived two cottages down and liked punk music as much as she did, though maybe for different reasons. She didn't get back to her egg until bedtime that night.

"What happens to you after I've made my wish?" she asked after she'd taken Arnold out of the egg.

I go away.

Marguerite asked, "Where to?" before she really thought about what she was saying, but this time Arnold didn't get upset.

To be someone else's wish, he said.

"And after that?"

Well, after they've made their wish, I'll go on to the next and the next …

"It sounds kind of boring."

Oh, no. I get to meet all sorts of interesting people.

Marguerite scratched her nose. She'd gotten a mosquito bite right on the end of it and felt very much like Pinocchio though she hadn't been telling any lies.

"Have you always been a wish?" she asked, not thinking again.

Arnold's voice grew so quiet that it was just a feathery touch in her mind. *I remember being something else … a long time ago …*

Marguerite leaned closer, as though that would help her hear him better. But there was a sudden feeling in her, as though Arnold had shaken himself out of his reverie.

Do you know what you're going to wish for yet? he asked briskly.

"Not exactly."

Well, just let me know when you're ready, he said and then he was gone again.

Marguerite sighed and put him away. This didn't seem to be at all the way this whole wishing business should go. Instead of feeling all excited about being able to ask for any one thing—*anything!*—she felt guilty because she kept making Arnold feel bad. Mind you, she thought, he did seem to be a gloomy sort of a genie when you came right down to it.

She fell asleep wondering if he looked the same wherever he went to when he left her as he did when she held him in her hand.

Somehow his ticklish, raspy voice didn't quite go with the lumpy clay figure that lay inside the brass egg. She supposed she'd never know.

As the summer progressed they became quite good friends, in an odd sort of way. Marguerite took to carrying the egg around with her in a small quilted bag that she slung over her shoulder. At opportune moments, she'd take Arnold out and they'd talk about all sorts of things.

Arnold, Marguerite discovered, knew a lot that she hadn't supposed a genie would know. He was current with all the latest bands, seemed to have seen all the best movies, knew stories that could make her giggle uncontrollably or shiver with chills under her blankets late at night. If she didn't press him for information about his past, he proved to be the best friend a person could want and she found herself telling him things she'd never think of telling anyone else.

It got to the point where Marguerite forgot he was a wish. Which was fine until the day that she left her quilted cotton bag behind in a restaurant in Smiths Falls on a day's outing with her mother. She became totally panic-stricken until her mother took her back to the restaurant, but by then her bag was gone, and so was the egg, and with it Arnold.

Marguerite was inconsolable. She moped around for days and nothing that anyone could do could cheer her up. She missed Arnold passionately. Missed their long talks when she was supposed to be sleeping. Missed the weight of his egg in her shoulder bag and the companionable presence of just knowing he was there. And also, she realized, she'd missed her chance of using her wish.

She could have had anything she wanted. She could have asked for piles of money. For fame and fortune. To be a lead singer in a rock band. To be a famous actor and star in all kinds of movies. She could have wished that Arnold would stay with her forever. Instead, jerk that she was, she'd never used the wish and now she had nothing. How could she be so stupid?

"Oh," she muttered one night in her bed. "I wish ... I wish ..."

She paused then, feeling a familiar tickle in her head.

Did you finally decide on your wish? Arnold asked.

Marguerite sat up so suddenly that she knocked over her water glass on the night table. Luckily it was empty.

"Arnold?" she asked, looking around. "Are you here?"

Well, not exactly here, *as it were, but I can hear you.*

"Where have you been?"

Waiting for you to make your wish.

"I've really missed you," Marguerite said. She patted her comforter with eager hands, trying to find Arnold's egg. "How did you get back here?"

I'm not exactly here, Arnold said.

"How come you never talked to me when I've been missing you all this time?"

I really can't initiate these things, Arnold explained. *It gets rather complicated, but even though my egg's with someone else, I can't really be their wish until I've finished being yours.*

"So we can still talk and be friends even though I've lost the egg?"

Not exactly. I can fulfill your wish, but since I'm not with *you, as it were, I can't really stay unless you're ready to make your wish.*

"You can't?" Marguerite wailed.

Afraid not. I don't make the rules, you know.

"I've got it," Marguerite said. And she did have it too. If she wanted to keep Arnold with her, all she had to do was wish for him to always be her friend. Then no one could take him away from her. They'd always be together.

"I wish …" she began.

But that didn't seem quite right, she realized. She gave her bleached forelock a nervous tug. It wasn't right to *make* someone be your friend. But if she didn't do that, if she wished something else, then Arnold would just go off and be somebody else's wish. Oh, if only things didn't have to be so complicated. Maybe she should just wish herself to the moon and be done with all her problems. She could lie there and stare at the world from a nice long distance away while she slowly asphyxiated. That would solve everything.

She felt the telltale feeling in her mind that let her know that Arnold was leaving again.

"Wait," she said, "I haven't made my wish yet."

The feeling stopped. *Then you've decided?* Arnold asked.

She hadn't, but as soon as he asked, she realized that there was only one fair wish she could make.

"I wish you were free," she said.

The feeling that was Arnold moved blurrily inside her.

You what? he asked.

"I wish you were free. I *can* wish that, can't I?"

Yes, but ... Wouldn't you rather have something, well, something for yourself?

"This *is* for myself," Marguerite said. "Your being free would be the best thing I could wish for because you're my friend and I don't want you to be trapped any more." She paused for a moment, brow wrinkling. "Or is there a rule against that?"

No rule, Arnold said softly. His ticklish voice bubbled with excitement. *No rule at all against it.*

"Then that's my wish," Marguerite said.

Inside her mind, she felt a sensation like a tiny whirlwind spinning around and around. It was like Arnold's voice and an autumn leaves smell and a kaleidoscope of dervishing lights, all wrapped up in one whirling sensation.

Free! Arnold called from the centre of that whirligig. *Free free free!*

A sudden weight was in Marguerite's hand and she saw that the brass egg had appeared there. It lay open in her palm, the faded velvet spilled out of it. It seemed so very small to hold so much happiness, but fluttering on tiny wings was the clay crow, rising up in a spin that twinned Arnold's presence in Marguerite's mind.

Her fingers closed around the brass egg as Arnold doubled, then tripled his size in an explosion of black feathers. His voice was like a chorus of bells, ringing and ringing between Marguerite's ears. Then with an exuberant caw, he stroked the air with his wings, flew out the cottage window, and was gone.

Marguerite sat quietly, staring out the window and holding the brass egg. A big grin stretched her lips. There was something so *right* about what she'd just done that she felt an overwhelming sense of happiness herself, as though she'd been the one trapped in a treadmill of wishes in a brass egg, and Arnold had been the one to free *her*.

At last she reached out and picked up from the comforter a small glossy black feather that Arnold had left behind. Wrapping it in the old velvet, she put it into the brass egg and screwed the egg shut once more.

That September a new family moved in next door with a boy her age named Arnold. Marguerite was delighted and, though her parents were surprised, she and the new boy became best friends almost immediately. She showed him the egg one day that winter and wasn't at all surprised that the feather she still kept in it was the exact same shade of black as her new friend's hair.

Arnold stroked the feather with one finger when she let him see it. He smiled at her and said, "I had a wish once ..."

Activities

1. If you had one wish, what would it be? Write a personal essay in which you discuss your wish. Give your reasons for choosing this wish and explain how it would change your life.

2. Arnold has a lot in common with Marguerite. Create a chart to compare the two characters. Then use the information in the chart to write a paragraph explaining why you think the author gave these two characters such similarities. In what way might Arnold symbolize a part of Marguerite?

3. Marguerite's parents are worried about her and her involvement with her imaginary friend Arnold. Work with a partner to write a dialogue that might take place between one of her parents and their family therapist. Make sure your dialogue uses information from the story. Present your dialogue to the class. Use the dialogue interpretations as a starting point to discuss Marguerite's experiences.

Messages Are

What message is the image and slogan on this mousepad sending? What other slogans or images appear on mousepads, and why do you think they were chosen?

INNOVATION

The best way to predict the future... is to create it.

Bayou Dragonfly

Summon Insect

Flying; swampwalk *(If defending player controls any swamps, this creature is unblockable.)*

"Like a sugar stick with wings!"
—Squee, goblin cabin hand

Illus. DiTerlizzi   1/1

Consider this creature's special powers. People of all ages enjoy playing games. What do people gain from playing games, and what might the purpose of this game be?

Everywhere!

KILL BIRDS

SAVE BIRDS

Every year more birds are killed hitting lit buildings than were lost during the entire EXXON Valdez disaster. So turn off your office lights at night. You'll be saving a lot more than energy.

WWF
CANADA
Their future is our future.

For more info call: 1·800·26·PANDA

Sometimes very simple images convey powerful messages. This public service poster dramatizes how turning off lights at night in office buildings saves migrating birds from becoming disoriented and flying into them. Why would a gesture as simple as turning off lights be up for debate?

B 4 U wish 4 any one thing, first examine how happy are those who already have it.

Consider the wisdom of this message. A fortune cookie is one example of a cultural tradition. What messages are contained in cultural traditions? Describe some of the traditions or symbols that are used in your culture.

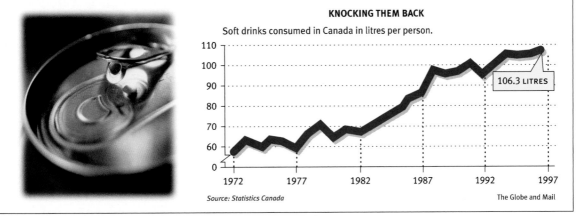

KNOCKING THEM BACK

Soft drinks consumed in Canada in litres per person.

106.3 LITRES

Source: Statistics Canada

The Globe and Mail

What do the figures in this graph suggest? Do these statistics alarm you? Why was the information it conveys set up in the form of a graph?

Dracula's Dinner

You have about 100 000 kilometres of blood vessels in your body—laid end-to-end, that's enough to circle Earth 2.5 times! There are three different kinds of vessels: arteries, veins, and capillaries. Arteries carry blood away from the heart; veins carry blood back to the heart. Tiny hair-like capillaries connect the smallest arteries with the smallest veins. Capillaries are so tiny, red blood cells have to squeeze through them single file. You can use bath beads and a few other supplies to see how red blood cells fit through capillaries.

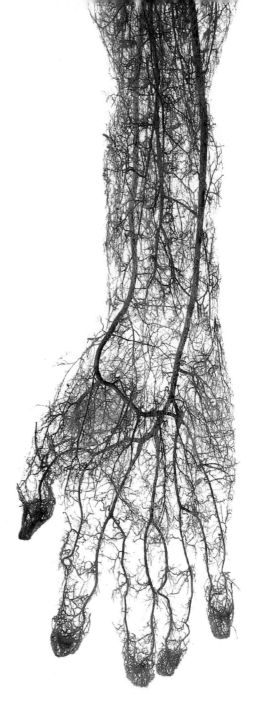

German anatomy professor Gunther von Hagens has developed a post-mortem preservation technique called "plastination." Here, the arterial blood vessels in a human forearm were drained and then injected with a coloured polymer, after which the surrounding tissue was stripped away.

Materials

- 3 big glass jars
- ice cream bucket, big mixing bowl, or sink
- salt
- food colouring
- box of wallpaper paste
- water
- Vaseline (petroleum jelly)
- funnel (The funnel we used had a spout with a 19 mm inside diameter. If you can't find one with this measurement, get one of your parents to cut an old funnel until it's the right size.)
- bath beads (see-through or clear ones work best)

Before You Start

- In this experiment, the funnel acts like a capillary.
- The round bath beads are red blood cells. Try to push a bath bead (blood cell) through the funnel (capillary). Right now the round beads will not fit through the funnel—if they do, your funnel spout is too big.

Instructions

1. Fill a jar with 2 cups of cold water.
2. Add 3 tablespoons of salt and a few drops of blue food colouring.
3. Fill a second jar with 2 cups of hot water.
4. Add 3 tablespoons of salt and a few drops of red food colouring.
5. Mix 1 cup of wallpaper paste with $2\frac{1}{4}$ cups of water in the third jar. The mixture should look like mashed potatoes.

Now you can experiment with the different mixtures to find out which ones help the bath bead (red blood cell) move through the funnel (capillary). Of course, put the funnel over a bucket, bowl, or sink so you don't spill liquid everywhere. Before you start, try to figure out which mixtures will be the most helpful.

Ideas

1. Try covering a bath bead with Vaseline. The bead gets pretty slippery, but it's still larger than the funnel. Does the lubrication allow the bead to slide through the funnel without breaking?
2. Soak a bath bead in the cold (blue) salt water for a few seconds. The bead may contract a bit. Does it fit through the funnel? Or does it just dissolve and break?
3. Soak a bath bead in the hot (red) salt water for a few seconds. The bead gets squishy—like when you use it in a bathtub full of hot water. Is the bead squishy enough to fit through the funnel? What happens to the shape? Does it break?
4. Soak a bath bead in wallpaper paste for about 20 minutes. What does it look like now? The bead should look like a red

blood cell—like a jelly doughnut. This shape is called a biconcave disc, which means that it curves inward in the middle. As with red blood cells, the bath bead's great jelly-doughnut shape allows it to fit through the funnel (the capillary). Why? The cellulose from the wallpaper paste passed through the thin skin of the bath bead making the bead very squishy. But it's not any weaker so it doesn't dissolve like the others you tried.

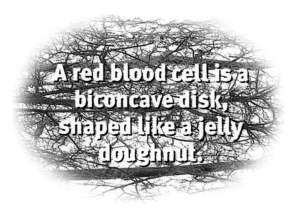

A red blood cell is a biconcave disk, shaped like a jelly doughnut.

Afterward

Notice how the surface of the bath bead stretched after soaking in the paste. Even though the bead still has the same amount of liquid inside, the surface area of the bead increased. The large surface area and biconcave shape allow many more oxygen molecules to come in contact with the surface of the red blood cell, making it an effective oxygen carrier.

Some people have a condition called sickle cell anemia. Their red blood cells look like crescent moons or sickles instead of like jelly doughnuts. Sickle cells can get stuck in tiny capillaries, blocking blood flow to different parts of the body. There is not yet any cure for this often painful and sometimes deadly disease.

Blood Bits

- There are about 25 trillion red blood cells in the human body!
- On average red blood cells live for four months.
- The body makes about 200 billion red blood cells every day to replace the millions that die every second!
- Red blood cells are about 7.5 micrometres wide; the smallest capillaries are only 5 micrometres wide.
- Red blood cells cannot reproduce because they have no nucleus. When red blood cells get worn out and no longer carry oxygen very well, they are destroyed in the liver, spleen, and bone marrow. All is not lost, however, because parts of the red blood cells are recycled to make new red blood cells.
- Go with the flow! Red blood cells do not move by themselves. They get swept along by the blood flow.

Take a Pulse

Do you know someone who acts more dead than alive? Prove they have a pulse! You can feel a pulse every time an artery stretches a tiny bit to allow blood to pass through it. It's easiest to feel a pulse where an artery is just below the skin: the back of the knee, the wrist, the side of the neck.

Put two fingers across your neck. Count the number of pulses you feel in a minute. That's the pulse—it's the same as the number of heartbeats in a minute. It will probably be around 90 beats per minute (an adult's will be around 70 beats per minute).

The pulse speeds up when you get excited or when you exercise. Do some jumping jacks for a few seconds and check your pulse again—it will be about two times as fast as before. Why? Your heart is pumping faster, sending more oxygen to hard-working muscles.

> ## Red blood cells:
> - **are made by the body at a rate of about 200 billion a day**
> - **are about 7.5 micrometres wide**
> - **live for about 4 months**

Activities

1. Explain the title of this experiment. What effect does this title have? What other techniques does the author use, and for what purpose?

2. Carefully read the details of the first paragraph. Draw a diagram to show the description of how blood vessels are interconnected. Label your drawing. You might wish to colour it for effect.

3. Complete the experiment as explained in the article. Use a science lab report format to present your findings. If you are unable to do the experiment, you can still complete the activity by carefully reading the information in the article. Include sections on purpose, apparatus, procedure, observations, calculations/diagrams, conclusions, questions that remain for further study.

When Jannies Visited Mary West Pratt

Activities

1. "Jannies" were "mummers," actors in traditional masked mimes, who often travelled from one community to the other. Imagine that you are the child under the table in the watercolour. How do you feel when the Jannies come to call? Describe your feelings in a well-edited paragraph.

2. Find a piece of music that you think matches this painting. "The Mummers' Dance" by Loreena Mckennitt would be an ideal choice. To analyse how the music matches the painting, develop a chart to compare the techniques used and the effects created in both.

Strokes of Genius

LESTER DAVID

Focus Your Learning
Reading this article
will help you:
- write a persuasive
  paragraph
- organize
  information
- develop ideas for
  a new invention

There are thousands of short people whose feet cannot reach the floor when they sit. Carrying a footstool is too cumbersome, so Jacob Rabinow of Bethesda, Maryland, hit upon a solution for a short friend. He attached two pieces of sheet aluminum onto a hollowed-out book, which, when extended, formed a lightweight, portable, collapsible footrest.

A Long Island, N.Y., woman recently visited New York City to apply for a visa. After a long trip and three hours of waiting in line at the consulate, the whole day was shot. Just ahead of her was a man holding a fistful of applications. He was employed by LendaHand—a company that helps busy people with this and other onerous chores. The brainchild of New Yorkers Oscar Allen and Donald Eggena, LendaHand now has 150 employees who queue up for hire at ticket offices, motor-vehicle bureaus, banks, supermarkets—places where lines can try anyone's temper.

Why couldn't *you* have come up with these resourceful ideas?

You could have, if you had applied a few basic principles followed by all successful inventors and originators of new ideas.

Together, these rules add up to creative thinking—which is not, as most people suppose, a mysterious gift possessed by a superior few. Astonishing as it may sound, each of us has this faculty.

"Creative behaviour is inherent in human nature," says Professor Sam Glucksberg of Princeton University. "Our research shows that people can be trained to increase their creativity."

Let's look at the birth of a few of those gadgets that seem so obvious now that they're here. How can *you* think creatively and develop little wonders of your own?

1. Fill a need

Those who succeed follow one important principle: give 'em what they don't have. Until Hyman L. Lipman of Philadelphia came along, people would rub out their writing with small chunks of India rubber, which kept getting lost. Lipman simply cemented a piece of rubber onto the top of a standard wood pencil. His stroke of genius continues to help those of us who make mistakes.

One day Conrad Hubert stared in fascination at a glowing flower pot a friend had made. Hubert's friend had put a battery and bulb inside the pot that lit up the blooms when a switch was turned on. Hubert then adapted the glowing pot into something much more useful. He put batteries and bulb inside a tube and gave the world its first flashlight.

2. Exploit a frustration

What bothers you, frustrates you, angers you, as you go about your day? King Gillette was tired of sharpening his straight razor, so he invented the safety razor with a disposable blade. Frederick W. Smith was fed up with slow mail, so he developed the concept of overnight delivery, which grew into Federal Express.

Chester Greenwood suffered from frostbitten ears in the sub-zero temperatures of western Maine. He attached fur cups to both ends of a wire and bent the contraption around his head. Orders for earmuffs soon came in from all over.

3. Use your know-how

"A successful inventor should build on his or her unique skills. But you don't have to be a full-fledged, card-carrying expert," says Tom Berquist, an idea man best known for his successful children's novelty candies.

Kaaydah Schatten of Toronto noticed that ceilings in factories and commercial buildings were coated with bacteria-laden grime and grease that often could not be removed. Schatten, an amateur chemist, used her know-how to develop a special cleaning solution that could be blasted in a high-pressure mist at ceilings. Dirt particles drift to the floor and are vacuumed away. Six years later her company, Ceiling Doctor International, is selling franchises worldwide.

Gerald E. Keinath's expertise lay in developing businesses for others. When he learned about a new process that can quickly fix holes and cracks in glass, Keinath decided to create a business for himself. Wouldn't drivers leap at repairing windshields at half the cost? Today his Minneapolis-based Novus, Inc. franchises and dealerships rack up more than [U.S.] $35 million in annual sales.

4. Finally, think small

Your ideas don't have to be big to be creative. The Frisbee didn't change the world, but it gave people loads of fun and made a mint. The adhesive bandage, safety pin, paper cup, and soda can pop-top were "small" ideas. Still, they were prime examples of imagination, curiosity, common sense, and hard work—all blended to fill a need, solve a problem, and make life a bit better.

Activities

1. The author believes that "creative behaviour is inherent in human nature." Do you agree? Why or why not? Write a paragraph explaining your point of view. Use examples from the past and present to support your answer.

2. With a partner, list five products or gadgets that are found in many homes today. Explain their success on a chart with categories shown below. Follow the example.

3. Work with a partner. Use the four categories shown in the chart to help you think of a new invention. Brainstorm ideas and then experiment with ideas until you are happy with one that you would like to develop more fully. Then develop a jingle or other commercial to advertise the product. Present your product and its commercial to the class. Be prepared to explain what needs your product helps to fill.

Product	Need it fills	Problem it helps to solve	Uses know-how	Think small
hair dryer	dries wet hair	dries hair quickly, so one can go out sooner	uses concept of fan and heating element	can fit into a small drawer

Northern Life

DOUG MCLARTY

My five-year-old son asked me a little while ago about dreams, and if they come true. Not to disappoint him I answered, slowly, with some thought as to how I might be able to relay my experience to him in a way that would not bore or confuse the question at hand.

"Son," I said, "As a young boy just like you I spent a lot of time dreaming of things around me, and as I got older the dreams got bigger and more adventurous. But one

The Indian in Transition Daphne Odjig

of my favourite dreams was of the North, the arctic regions of Canada.

"In school we learnt of the Arctic with its vast beauty and open skies. We studied about how in the spring, the sun would rise above the horizon, casting colours of orange and red against the clouds. The sun continuing to rise each day higher and longer until the daylight was the same at one o'clock in the morning as one o'clock in the afternoon.

"I dreamed of playing outside all day and all night, not stopping for anything as the sun shone down twenty-four hours a day. Playing along the shore of the ocean and watching the long, flat horizon for seals or the occasional whale that may pass by the inlet.

"Then as the night breeze started I dreamed of riding on the land with my four-wheeler, twisting and dashing between the little lakes and wetlands to the top of the gravel esker. Castles of the arctic, where you could see for endless miles. The land stretching in all directions dotted with lakes and grass lands, rolling hills and streams glistening with fish.

"I would be able to stop for breaks and stoop down to my knees, take a fill of low bush blueberries and blackberries nestled between clumps of small flowers and rocks for protection from the winds and hot summer sun.

"When I was bigger my dreams turned to the fishing of the greatest fish of them all: the arctic char. Hooked onto the line for the fight of my life, as the great silver sides flipped and rose out of the waters to catch the sun in a blinding flash of pride. The final battle reward of a lunch cooked over an open fire while the cool waters of the river flowed over the rocks was music to my ears.

"I dreamed of the fall weather coming, the fast approach of winter and the snow falling. Travel with my snow machine fast and as far as I could go in search of the caribou. Herds of animals numbering more than I could count. I dreamed of moving right up to the herd, and then over in among the caribou, arms reaching away from the great horned animals. Hundreds and hundreds of them in a single group.

"I dreamed of travelling over the snow blown into drifts as hard as cement and as tall as buildings, allowing us to camp out on the land protected behind the great drifts.

At the end of my arctic dream I was watching the dancing of the aurora borealis filled with colours swirling and curling as though someone was sweeping them as dust on the floor and the stars glistening, flashing little sparkles in the darkness, too many to be counted.

"Son, to dream," I paused to conclude my answer to my son but his eyes and the smile on his face overtook my thoughts—you could almost see his mind whirling. His response to my pause was the answer that I needed but could not find.

"Daddy, is that the picture of the fish you caught in your dreams?"

I stood back, took the picture off the wall, glanced up at him, and concluded, "Yes, my son, dreams do come true."

Activities

1. Pick one of the first ten paragraphs in this essay. Rewrite the paragraph, omitting all the descriptive words. Read your paragraph and the original paragraph to the class. Discuss how the descriptive words enhance the writing.

2. Write your own short non-descriptive paragraph about a well-known location. Read your paragraph aloud to a partner.

   Read it one more time, adding descriptive details. Have your partner try to identify the location as you add details. Share your paragraphs with the class. Work as a class to develop criteria for effective descriptive writing.

3. Make a collage to illustrate this essay. Try to convey the images and atmosphere suggested by the author.

The Protected Areas Vision   Partnership for Public Lands

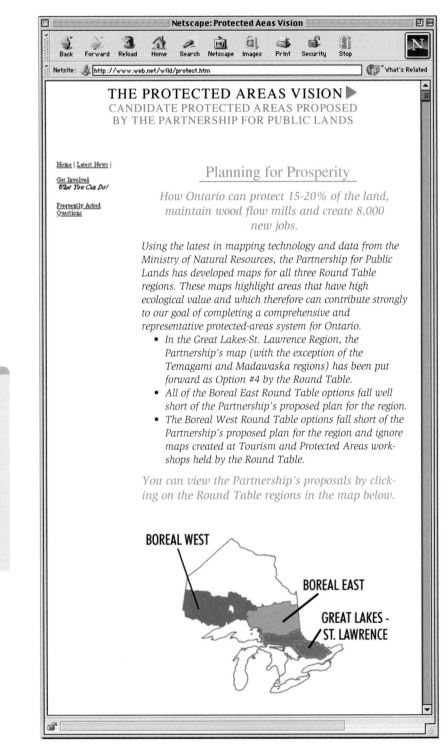

Focus Your Learning
Reading this web page
will help you:

- recognize the power of
  media
- summarize an
  argument
- look for bias
- discuss an issue,
  giving support for
  different viewpoints

Netscape: Protected Aeas Vision

Back Forward Reload Home Search Netscape Images Print Security Stop

Netsite: http://www.web.net/wild/protect.htm   What's Related

THE PROTECTED AREAS VISION ▶
CANDIDATE PROTECTED AREAS PROPOSED
BY THE PARTNERSHIP FOR PUBLIC LANDS

Home | Latest News |

Get Involved
What You Can Do!

Frequently Asked
Questions

Planning for Prosperity

*How Ontario can protect 15-20% of the land,
maintain wood flow mills and create 8,000
new jobs.*

Using the latest in mapping technology and data from the
Ministry of Natural Resources, the Partnership for Public
Lands has developed maps for all three Round Table
regions. These maps highlight areas that have high
ecological value and which therefore can contribute strongly
to our goal of completing a comprehensive and
representative protected-areas system for Ontario.

- In the Great Lakes-St. Lawrence Region, the
  Partnership's map (with the exception of the
  Temagami and Madawaska regions) has been put
  forward as Option #4 by the Round Table.
- All of the Boreal East Round Table options fall well
  short of the Partnership's proposed plan for the region.
- The Boreal West Round Table options fall short of the
  Partnership's proposed plan for the region and ignore
  maps created at Tourism and Protected Areas work-
  shops held by the Round Table.

*You can view the Partnership's proposals by click-
ing on the Round Table regions in the map below.*

BOREAL WEST

BOREAL EAST

GREAT LAKES -
ST. LAWRENCE

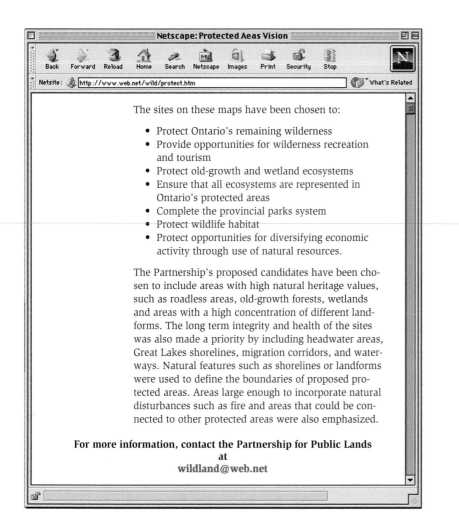

The sites on these maps have been chosen to:

- Protect Ontario's remaining wilderness
- Provide opportunities for wilderness recreation and tourism
- Protect old-growth and wetland ecosystems
- Ensure that all ecosystems are represented in Ontario's protected areas
- Complete the provincial parks system
- Protect wildlife habitat
- Protect opportunities for diversifying economic activity through use of natural resources.

The Partnership's proposed candidates have been chosen to include areas with high natural heritage values, such as roadless areas, old-growth forests, wetlands and areas with a high concentration of different landforms. The long term integrity and health of the sites was also made a priority by including headwater areas, Great Lakes shorelines, migration corridors, and waterways. Natural features such as shorelines or landforms were used to define the boundaries of proposed protected areas. Areas large enough to incorporate natural disturbances such as fire and areas that could be connected to other protected areas were also emphasized.

For more information, contact the Partnership for Public Lands at wildland@web.net

Activities

1. All web pages, just like other pieces of writing, are written for a purpose and an audience. Identify the purpose and audience of this web page.

2. What are your first impressions of this web site? List the arguments that you notice as you scan the page. Summarize the conclusions that you draw using this site as your only source of information.

3. Do you agree that wild areas should be protected from industrial activity? If so, what ecological, social, and economic considerations or values do you think should be used to identify which natural sites should be protected?

The Veldt RAY BRADBURY

"George, I wish you'd look at the nursery."

"What's wrong with it?"

"I don't know."

"Well, then."

"I just want you to look at it, is all, or call a psychologist in to look at it."

"What would a psychologist want with a nursery?"

"You know very well what he'd want." His wife paused in the middle of the kitchen and watched the stove busy humming to itself, making supper for four.

"It's just that the nursery is different now than it was."

"All right, let's have a look."

They walked down the hall of their soundproofed Happylife Home, which had cost them thirty thousand dollars installed, this house which clothed and fed and rocked them to sleep and played and sang and was good to them. Their approach sensitized a switch somewhere and the nursery light flicked on when they came within three metres of it. Similarly, behind them, in the halls, lights went on and off as they left them behind, with a soft automaticity.

"Well," said George Hadley.

They stood on the thatched floor of the nursery. It was twelve metres across by twelve metres long and nine metres high; it had cost half again as much as the rest of the house. "But nothing's too good for our children," George had said.

The nursery was silent. It was empty as a jungle glade at hot high noon. The walls were blank and two-dimensional. Now, as George and Lydia Hadley stood in the centre of the room, the walls began to purr and recede into crystalline distance, it seemed, and presently an African veldt appeared, in three dimensions; on all sides, in colour, reproduced to the final pebble and bit of straw. The ceiling above them became a deep sky with a hot yellow sun.

George Hadley felt the perspiration start on his brow.

"Let's get out of the sun," he said. "This is a little too real. But I don't see anything wrong."

"Wait a moment, you'll see," said his wife.

Now the hidden odorophonics were beginning to blow a wind of odour at the two people in the middle of the baked veldtland. The hot straw smell of lion grass, the cool green smell of the hidden water hole, the great rusty smell of animals, the smell of dust like a red paprika in the hot air. And now the sounds: the thump of distant antelope feet on grassy sod, the papery rustling of vultures. A shadow passed through the sky. The shadow flickered on George Hadley's upturned, sweating face.

"Filthy creatures," he heard his wife say.

"The vultures."

"You see, there are the lions, far over, that way. Now they're on their way to the water hole. They've just been eating," said Lydia. "I don't know what."

"Some animal." George Hadley put his hand up to shield off the burning light from his squinted eyes. "A zebra or a baby giraffe, maybe."

"Are you sure?" His wife sounded peculiarly tense.

"No, it's a little late to be sure," he said, amused. "Nothing over there I can see but cleaned bone, and the vultures dropping for what's left."

"Did you hear that scream?" she asked.

"No."

"About a minute ago?"

"Sorry, no."

The lions were coming. And again George Hadley was filled with admiration for the mechanical genius who had conceived this room. A miracle of efficiency selling for an absurdly low price. Every home should have one. Oh, occasionally they frightened you with their clinical accuracy, they startled you, gave you a twinge, but most of the time what fun for everyone, not only your own son and daughter, but for yourself when you felt like a quick jaunt to a foreign land, a quick change of scenery. Well, here it was!

And here were the lions now, five metres away, so real, so feverishly and startlingly real that you could feel the prickling fur on your hand, and your mouth was stuffed with the dusty upholstery smell of their heated pelts, and the yellow of them was in your eyes like the yellow of an exquisite French tapestry, the yellows of lions and summer grass, and the sound of the matted lion lungs exhaling on the silent noontide, and the smell of meat from the panting, dripping mouths.

The lions stood looking at George and Lydia Hadley with terrible green-yellow eyes.

"Watch out!" screamed Lydia.

The lions came running at them.

Lydia bolted and ran. Instinctively, George sprang after her. Outside, in the hall, with the door slammed, he was laughing and she was crying, and they both stood appalled at the other's reaction.

"George!"

"Lydia! Oh, my dear poor sweet Lydia!"

"They almost got us!"

"Walls, Lydia, remember; crystal walls, that's all they are. Oh, they look real, I must admit—Africa in your parlour—but it's all dimensional, superreactionary, supersensitive colour film and mental tape film behind glass screens. It's all odorophonics and sonics, Lydia. Here's my handkerchief."

"I'm afraid." She came to him and put her body against him and cried steadily. "Did you see? Did you *feel*? It's too real."

"Now, Lydia …"

"You've got to tell Wendy and Peter not to read any more on Africa."

"Of course—of course." He patted her.

"Promise?"

"Sure."

"And lock the nursery for a few days until I get my nerves settled."

"You know how difficult Peter is about that. When I punished him a month ago by locking the nursery for even a few hours—the tantrum he threw! And Wendy too. They *live* for the nursery."

"It's got to be locked, that's all there is to it."

"All right." Reluctantly he locked the huge door. "You've been working too hard. You need a rest."

"I don't know—I don't know," she said, blowing her nose, sitting down in a chair that immediately began to rock and comfort her. "Maybe I don't have enough to do. Maybe I have time to think too much. Why don't we shut the whole house off for a few days and take a vacation?"

"You mean you want to fry my eggs for me?"

"Yes." She nodded.

"And darn my socks?"

"Yes." A frantic, watery-eyed nodding.

"And sweep the house?"

"Yes, yes—oh, yes!"

"But I thought that's why we bought this house, so we wouldn't have to do anything?"

"That's just it. I feel like I don't belong here. The house is wife and mother now and nursemaid. Can I compete with an African veldt? Can I give a bath and scrub the children as efficiently or quickly as the automatic scrub bath can? I cannot. And it isn't just me. It's you. You've been awfully nervous lately."

"I suppose I have been smoking too much."

"You look as if you didn't know what to do with yourself in this house, either. You smoke a little more every morning and drink a little more every afternoon and need a little more sedative every night. You're beginning to feel unnecessary too."

"Am I?" He paused and tried to feel into himself to see what was really there.

"Oh, George!" She looked beyond him, at the nursery door. "Those lions can't get out of there, can they?"

He looked at the door and saw it tremble as if something had jumped against it from the other side.

"Of course not," he said.

At dinner they ate alone, for Wendy and Peter were at a special plastic carnival across town and had televised home to say they'd be late, to go ahead eating. So George Hadley, bemused, sat watching the dining-room table produce warm dishes of food from its mechanical interior.

"We forgot the ketchup," he said.

"Sorry," said a small voice within the table, and ketchup appeared.

As for the nursery, thought George Hadley, it won't hurt for the children to be locked out of it awhile. Too much of anything isn't good

for anyone. And it was clearly indicated that the children had been spending a little too much time on Africa. That sun. He could feel it on his neck, still, like a hot paw. And the lions. And the smell of blood. Remarkable how the nursery caught the telepathic emanations of the children's minds and created life to fill their every desire. The children thought lions, and there were lions. The children thought zebras, and there were zebras. Sun—sun. Giraffes—giraffes. Death and death.

That last. He chewed tastelessly on the meat that the table had cut for him. Death thoughts. They were awfully young, Wendy and Peter, for death thoughts. Or, no, you were never too young, really. Long before you knew what death was you were wishing it on someone else. When you were two years old, you were shooting people with cap pistols.

But this—the long, hot African veldt—the awful death in the jaws of a lion. And repeated again and again.

"Where are you going?"

He didn't answer Lydia. Preoccupied, he let the lights glow softly on ahead of him, extinguished behind him as he padded to the nursery door. He listened against it. Far away, a lion roared.

He unlocked the door and opened it. Just before he stepped inside, he heard a faraway scream. And then another roar from the lions, which subsided quickly.

He stepped into Africa. How many times in the last year had he opened this door and found Wonderland, Alice, the Mock Turtle, or Aladdin and his Magical Lamp, or Jack Pumpkinhead of Oz, or Dr. Dolittle, or the cow jumping over a very real-appearing moon—all the delightful contraptions of a make-believe world. How often had he seen Pegasus flying in the sky ceiling, or seen fountains of red fireworks, or heard angel voices singing. But now, this yellow hot Africa, this bake oven with murder in the heat. Perhaps Lydia was right. Perhaps they needed a little vacation from the fantasy which was growing a bit too real for ten-year-old children. It was all right to exercise one's mind with gymnastic fantasies, but when the lively child mind settled on *one* pattern …? It seemed that, at a distance, for the past month, he had

heard lions roaring, and smelled their strong odour seeping as far away as his study door. But, being busy, he had paid it no attention.

George Hadley stood on the African grassland alone. The lions looked up from their feeding, watching him. The only flaw to the illusion was the open door through which he could see his wife, far down the dark hall, like a framed picture, eating her dinner abstractedly.

"Go away," he said to the lions.

They did not go.

He knew the principle of the room exactly. You sent out your thoughts. Whatever you thought would appear.

"Let's have Aladdin and his lamp," he snapped.

The veldtland remained; the lions remained.

"Come on, room! I demand Aladdin!" he said.

Nothing happened. The lions mumbled in their baked pelts.

"Aladdin!"

He went back to dinner. "The fool room's out of order," he said. "It won't respond."

"Or—"

"Or what?"

"Or it *can't* respond," said Lydia, "because the children have thought about Africa and lions and killing so many days that the room's in a rut."

"Could be."

"Or Peter's set it to remain that way."

"*Set* it?"

"He may have got into the machinery and fixed something."

"Peter doesn't know machinery."

"He's a wise one for ten. That I.Q. of his—"

"Nevertheless—"

"Hello, Mom. Hello, Dad."

The Hadleys turned. Wendy and Peter were coming in the front door, cheeks like peppermint candy, eyes like bright blue agate marbles, a smell of ozone on their jumpers from their trip in the helicopter.

"You're just in time for supper," said both parents.

"We're full of strawberry ice cream and hot dogs," said the children, holding hands. "But we'll sit and watch."

"Yes, come tell us about the nursery," said George Hadley.

The brother and sister blinked at him and then at each other. "Nursery?"

"All about Africa and everything," said the father with false joviality.

"I don't understand," said Peter.

"Your mother and I were just travelling through Africa with rod and reel: Tom Swift and his Electric Lion," said George Hadley.

"There's no Africa in the nursery," said Peter simply.

"Oh, come now, Peter. We know better."

"I don't remember any Africa," said Peter to Wendy. "Do you?"

"No."

"Run see and come tell."

She obeyed.

"Wendy, come back here!" said George Hadley, but she was gone. The house lights followed her like a flock of fireflies. Too late, he realized he had forgotten to lock the nursery door after his last inspection.

"Wendy'll look and come tell us," said Peter.

"She doesn't have to tell *me*. I've seen it."

"I'm sure you're mistaken, Father."

"I'm not, Peter. Come along now."

But Wendy was back. "It's not Africa," she said breathlessly.

"We'll see about this," said George Hadley, and they all walked down the hall together and opened the nursery door.

There was a green, lovely forest, a lovely river, a purple mountain, high voices singing, and Rima, lovely and mysterious, lurking in the trees with colourful flights of butterflies, like animated bouquets, lingering on her long hair. The African veldtland was gone. The lions were gone. Only Rima was here now, singing a song so beautiful that it brought tears to your eyes.

George Hadley looked in at the changed scene. "Go to bed," he said to the children.

They opened their mouths.

"You heard me," he said.

They went off to the air closet, where a wind sucked them like brown leaves up the flue to their slumber rooms.

George Hadley walked through the singing glade and picked up something that lay in the corner near where the lions had been. He walked slowly back to his wife.

"What is that?" she asked.

"An old wallet of mine," he said.

He showed it to her. The smell of hot grass was on it and the smell of a lion. There were drops of saliva on it, it had been chewed, and there were blood smears on both sides.

He closed the nursery door and locked it, tight.

In the middle of the night he was still awake and he knew his wife was awake. "Do you think Wendy changed it?" she said at last, in the dark room.

"Of course."

"Made it from a veldt into a forest and put Rima there instead of lions?"

"Yes."

"Why?"

"I don't know. But it's staying locked until I find out."

"How did your wallet get there?"

"I don't know anything," he said, "except that I'm beginning to be sorry we bought that room for the children. If children are neurotic at all, a room like that—"

"It's supposed to help them work off their neuroses in a healthful way."

"I'm starting to wonder." He stared at the ceiling.

"We've given the children everything they ever wanted. Is this our reward—secrecy, disobedience?"

"Who was it said, 'Children are carpets, they should be stepped on occasionally'? We've never lifted a hand. They're insufferable—let's admit it. They come and go when they like; they treat us as if *we* were offspring. They're spoiled and we're spoiled."

"They've been acting funny ever since you forbade them to take the rocket to New York a few months ago."

"They're not old enough to do that alone, I explained."

"Nevertheless, I've noticed they've been decidedly cool toward us since."

"I think I'll have David McClean come tomorrow morning to have a look at Africa."

"But it's not Africa now, it's Green Mansions country and Rima."

"I have a feeling it'll be Africa again before then."

A moment later they heard the screams.

Two screams. Two people screaming from downstairs. And then a roar of lions.

"Wendy and Peter aren't in their rooms," said his wife.

He lay in his bed with his beating heart. "No," he said. "They've broken into the nursery."

"Those screams—they sound familiar."

"Do they?"

"Yes, awfully."

And although their beds tried very hard, the two adults couldn't be rocked to sleep for another hour. A smell of cats was in the night air.

"Father?" said Peter.

"Yes."

Peter looked at his shoes. He never looked at his father any more, nor at his mother. "You aren't going to lock up the nursery for good, are you?"

"That all depends."

"On what?" snapped Peter.

"On you and your sister. If you intersperse this Africa with a little variety—oh, Sweden perhaps, or Denmark, or China—"

"I thought we were free to play as we wished."

"You are, within reasonable bounds."

"What's wrong with Africa, Father?"

"Oh, so now you admit you have been conjuring up Africa, do you?"

"I wouldn't want the nursery locked up," said Peter coldly. "Ever."

"Matter of fact, we're thinking of turning the whole house off for about a month. Live sort of a carefree one-for-all existence."

"That sounds dreadful! Would I have to tie my own shoes instead of letting the shoe tier do it? And brush my own teeth and comb my hair and give myself a bath?"

"It would be fun for a change, don't you think?"

"No, it would be horrid. I didn't like it when you took out the picture painter last month."

"That's because I wanted you to learn to paint all by yourself, son."

"I don't want to do anything but look and listen and smell; what else *is* there to do?"

"All right, go play in Africa."

"Will you shut off the house sometime soon?"

"We're considering it."

"I don't think you'd better consider it any more, Father."

"I won't have any threats from my son!"

"Very well." And Peter strolled off to the nursery.

"Am I on time?" said David McClean.

"Breakfast?" asked George Hadley.

"Thanks, had some. What's the trouble?"

"David, you're a psychologist."

"I should hope so."

"Well, then, have a look at our nursery. You saw it a year ago when you dropped by; did you notice anything peculiar about it then?"

"Can't say I did; the usual violences, a tendency toward a slight paranoia here or there, usual in children because they feel persecuted by parents constantly, but, oh, really nothing."

They walked down the hall. "I locked the nursery up," explained the father, "and the children broke back into it during the night. I let them stay so they could form the patterns for you to see."

There was a terrible screaming from the nursery.

"There it is," said George Hadley. "See what you make of it."

They walked in on the children without rapping.

The screams had faded. The lions were feeding.

"Run outside a moment, children," said George Hadley. "No, don't change the mental combination. Leave the walls as they are. Get!"

With the children gone, the two men stood studying the lions clustered at a distance, eating with great relish whatever it was they had caught.

"I wish I knew what it was," said George Hadley. "Sometimes I can almost see. Do you think if I brought high-powered binoculars here and—"

David McClean laughed dryly. "Hardly." He turned to study all four walls. "How long has this been going on?"

"A little over a month."

"It certainly doesn't *feel* good."

"I want facts, not feelings."

"My dear George, a psychologist never saw a fact in his life. He only hears about feelings; vague things. This doesn't feel good, I tell you. Trust my hunches and my instincts. I have a nose for something bad. This is very bad. My advice to you is to have the whole damn room torn down and your children brought to me every day during the next year for treatment."

"Is it that bad?"

"I'm afraid so. One of the original uses of these nurseries was so that we could study the patterns left on the walls by the child's mind, study at our leisure, and help the child. In this case, however, the room has become a channel toward—destructive thoughts, instead of a release away from them."

"Didn't you sense this before?"

"I sensed only that you had spoiled your children more than most. And now you're letting them down in some way. What way?"

"I wouldn't let them go to New York."

"What else?"

"I've taken a few machines from the house and threatened them, a month ago, with closing up the nursery unless they did their homework. I did close it for a few days to show I meant business."

"Ah, ha!"

"Does that mean anything?"

"Everything. Where before they had a Santa Claus now they have a Scrooge. Children prefer Santas. You've let this room and this house replace you and your wife in your children's affections. This room is their mother and father, far more important in their lives than their real parents. And now you come along and want to shut it off. No wonder there's hatred here. You can feel it coming out of the sky. Feel that sun. George, you'll have to change your life. Like too many others, you've built it around creature comforts. Why, you'd starve tomorrow if something went wrong in your kitchen. You wouldn't know how to tap an egg. Nevertheless, turn everything off. Start new. It'll take time. But we'll make good children out of bad in a year, wait and see."

"But won't the shock be too much for the children, shutting the room up abruptly, for good?"

"I don't want them going any deeper into this, that's all."

The lions were finished with their red feast.

The lions were standing on the edge of the clearing watching the two men.

"Now *I'm* feeling persecuted," said McClean. "Let's get out of here. I never have cared for these damned rooms. Make me nervous."

"The lions look real, don't they?" said George Hadley. "I don't suppose there's any way—"

"What?"

"—that they could *become* real?"

"Not that I know."

"Some flaw in the machinery, a tampering or something?"

"No."

They went to the door.

"I don't imagine the room will like being turned off," said the father.

"Nothing ever likes to die—even a room."

"I wonder if it hates me for wanting to switch it off?"

"Paranoia is thick around here today," said David McClean. "You can follow it like a spoor. Hello." He bent and picked up a bloody scarf. "This yours?"

"No." George Hadley's face was rigid. "It belongs to Lydia."

They went to the fuse box together and threw the switch that killed the nursery.

The two children were in hysterics. They screamed and pranced and threw things. They yelled and sobbed and swore and jumped at the furniture.

"You can't do that to the nursery, you can't!"

"Now, children."

The children flung themselves onto a couch, weeping.

"George," said Lydia Hadley, "turn on the nursery, just for a few moments. You can't be so abrupt."

"No."

"You can't be so cruel."

"Lydia, it's off, and it stays off. And the whole damn house dies as of here and now. The more I see of the mess we've put ourselves in, the more it sickens me. We've been contemplating our mechanical, electronic navels for too long. My God, how we need a breath of honest air!"

And he marched about the house turning off the voice clocks, the stoves, the heaters, the shoe shiners, the shoe lacers, the body scrubbers and swabbers and massagers, and every other machine he could put his hand to.

The house was full of dead bodies, it seemed. It felt like a mechanical cemetery. So silent. None of the humming hidden energy of machines waiting to function at the tap of a button.

"Don't let them do it!" wailed Peter at the ceiling, as if he was talking to the house, the nursery. "Don't let Father kill everything." He turned to his father. "Oh, I hate you!"

"Insults won't get you anywhere."

"I wish you were dead."

"We were, for a long while. Now we're going to really start living. Instead of being handled and massaged, we're going to *live*."

Wendy was still crying and Peter joined her again. "Just a moment, just one moment, just another moment of nursery," they wailed.

"Oh, George," said the wife, "it can't hurt."

"All right—all right, if they'll only just shut up. One minute, mind you, and then off forever."

"Daddy, Daddy, Daddy!" sang the children, smiling with wet faces.

"And then we're going on a vacation. David McClean is coming back in half an hour to help us move out and get to the airport. I'm going to dress. You turn the nursery on for a minute, Lydia, just a minute, mind you."

And the three of them went babbling off while he let himself be vacuumed upstairs through the air flue and set about dressing himself. A minute later Lydia appeared.

"I'll be glad when we get away," she sighed.

"Did you leave them in the nursery?"

"I wanted to dress too. Oh, that horrid Africa. What can they see in it?"

"Well, in five minutes we'll be on our way to Iowa. Lord, how did we ever get in this house? What prompted us to buy a nightmare?"

"Pride, money, foolishness."

"I think we'd better get downstairs before those kids get engrossed with those damned beasts again."

Just then they heard the children calling, "Daddy, Mommy, come quick—quick!"

They went downstairs in the air flue and ran down the hall. The children were nowhere in sight. "Wendy? Peter!"

They ran into the nursery. The veldtland was empty save for the lions waiting, looking at them. "Peter, Wendy?"

The door slammed.

"Wendy, Peter!"

George Hadley and his wife whirled and ran back to the door.

"Open the door!" cried George Hadley, trying the knob. "Why, they've locked it from the outside! Peter!" He beat at the door. "Open up!"

He heard Peter's voice outside, against the door.

"Don't let them switch off the nursery and the house," he was saying.

Mr. and Mrs. George Hadley beat at the door. "Now, don't be ridiculous, children. It's time to go. Mr. McClean'll be here in a minute and …"

And then they heard the sounds.

The lions on three sides of them, in the yellow veldt grass, padding through the dry straw, rumbling and roaring in their throats.

The lions.

Mr. Hadley looked at his wife and they turned and looked back at the beasts edging slowly forward, crouching, tails stiff.

Mr. and Mrs. Hadley screamed.

And suddenly they realized why those other screams had sounded familiar.

"Well, here I am," said David McClean in the nursery doorway. "Oh, hello." He stared at the two children seated in the centre of the open glade eating a little picnic lunch.

Beyond them was the water hole and the yellow veldtland; above was the hot sun. He began to perspire. "Where are your father and mother?"

The children looked up and smiled. "Oh, they'll be here directly."

"Good, we must get going." At a distance Mr. McClean saw the lions fighting and clawing and then quieting down to feed in silence under the shady trees.

He squinted at the lions with his hand up to his eyes.

Now the lions were done feeding. They moved to the water hole to drink.

A shadow flickered over Mr. McClean's hot face. Many shadows flickered. The vultures were dropping down the blazing sky.

"A cup of tea?" asked Wendy in the silence.

Activities

1. The theme of a text is often the author's message about human nature or society. What is Ray Bradbury's theme for this story? Work with a partner to list as many themes as you can think of. For each idea, give examples and reasons to support your thinking. Discuss your ideas with your classmates. Consider the futuristic setting of the story. Does this enhance or detract from the theme?

2. Considering what Bradbury has to say about human nature, write a list of instructions to Wendy and Peter's parents advising them of where they went wrong and what they should have done differently. Make sure you use examples from the story to justify your advice.

3. You have been hired to create a magazine advertisement for the nursery in this story. Reread the story looking for specific details and descriptions of the nursery. Once you have your list, sketch out a rough plan for your ad. Look through a few magazines to find ads, and notice what effects strike you as most persuasive. How can you include these elements in your ad? Share your rough draft with a partner for some suggestions for improvement as well as positive feedback. Once you have incorporated the suggestions for improvement, do a good copy. Post the ads around the classroom.

4. Imagine you are Wendy and Peter's grandparents. You now have responsibility for the children, and have inherited the house and nursery. Write a complaint letter to the makers of the nursery. Your letter should use correct business letter format. In the first paragraph, introduce the problem and explain what was promised. In the second paragraph, explain what went wrong and the results. In the third paragraph, suggest ways in which you might be compensated. Use specific details and examples from the story.

Dreams

BUDGE
WILSON

Taken from *The Killick* ©1995 Geoff Butler, published by Tundra Books.

I was sixteen years old when he took my dream away from me. It is not a small offence to be a stealer of dreams.

Our family lived in Mackerel Cove, a small fishing village on the South Shore of Nova Scotia. When I tell people that, when I point out the exact location, they look at me with a puzzled, almost incredulous expression. Sometimes that look is all I get. Other times, they give voice to their astonishment. "But how did you become what you are? How did you get from there to here?"

What do they think goes on in small fishing communities? Nothing? Do they assume that such places contain people with no brains, no ambition, no dreams? They look at me as though my skin had just turned green. As though I'd been cast in some inferior mould and had, by some miracle of agility or cussedness, found a way to jump out of it. By the time those questions started, I was a junior executive in an oil company, in the days before oil became a questionable commodity—in Toronto, where the mould is often even more fixed than elsewhere.

When I was a boy of eleven, the horizon was endless, physically and metaphorically. From our yellow frame house—which was perched on a hill, without the protection or impediment of trees—you could view the wide sea, stretching from the rocky point and behind Granite Island, disappearing beyond the edge of the sky, inviting dreams of any dimension. And in the foreground, four reefs threw their huge waves up into the air—wild, free.

I spent a lot of time sitting on the woodpile—when I was supposed to be cutting wood, piling wood, or carting wood—looking at the view. And thinking. Planning. Rumour had it that if you drew a straight line from our front door, right through the centre of that horizon, the line would eventually end up on the west coast of North Africa. How can Torontonians conclude that such an environment is limiting? They're lucky if they can see through the smog to the end of the block. I could go straight from the woodpile to Africa. Or I could turn left and wind up in Portugal.

And the wind. On that hill, where my great-grandfather had had the vision to build his house, the wind was always a factor. Even when it was not blowing. Then my mother would emerge into the sunshine or the fog, and take a deep breath. "Gone," she would announce. She hated the wind. She was from near Truro, where the slow, muddy Salmon River just limps along its banks, shining brown and slithery in the dead air. Dead air—that's what inlanders seem to want. Then they feel safe. Or peaceful. But those were two words that meant nothing to me at that time.

What is it about kids that makes them so blind and deaf for so long? Some of them, anyway. How can they go charging into life with such a certainty that all is well? Without, in fact, a passing thought as to whether it is or is not? It's just there. Mackerel are for jigging, the sea is for swimming, a boat is for rowing around in. The gulls are for watching, particularly on those days when the wind is up, when they just hang high in the air, motionless, wings wide, riding the storm. I was like that when I was eleven, sailing along with no effort, unconscious of the currents and turbulence that surrounded me.

Twelve seems to be a favourite time for waking up. What is so special about twelve that makes it such a hazardous, such a brittle age? No doubt it's partly because of all those puberty things—those unseen forces that begin to churn up your body, making it vulnerable to dangers that didn't even seem to exist before that time. And with the body, so goes the head and the heart.

All of a sudden (it really did seem to start happening all within the space of a day), I began to hear things. Things like the edge in my mother's voice, the ragged sound of my father's anger. Where had I been before? Too busy on the woodpile, in the boats, at the beach—*outside*. Or when inside, shut off by comic books, TV, the all-absorbing enjoyment of food. And lots of arguing and horsing around with my brothers and sisters, of whom there were five. But now, suddenly, the wind blew, and I heard it.

Once you have heard those sounds, your ears are permanently unplugged, and you cannot stop them up again. Same thing with the eyes. I began to see my mother's face as an objective thing. Not just *my mother*, a warm and blurry concept, but a face to watch and think about and read. It was pinched, dry-looking, with two vertical lines between the brows. Much of the time, I saw, she looked anxious or disenchanted. I didn't know the meaning of that word, back then, but I recognized the condition. She was thin and pale of skin—probably because she didn't like to be out in the wind—with a head of defeated-looking thin brown hair. I saw that for the first time too.

Within twenty-four hours of my awakening, I felt that I had

discovered and recognized everything. My mother, I knew, was worried about money—or about the extreme scarcity of it. That seemed a waste of time to me. There were fish in the sea, vegetables in the garden, loaves of bread in the oven, and second-hand clothes to be had at Frenchy's. But look again. Not just worry. Something else. And that, I knew, had to do with my father. I watched very carefully. He didn't ask for things. He demanded. "Gimme the sugar." "Let the dog out." "Eat your damn vegetables." He didn't praise. He criticized. "This soup is too cold." "There's a rip in them pants." And on pickling day, "Too blasted hot in this kitchen." As he made each one of these remarks, I would see a small contraction in those vertical lines on my mother's forehead. Not much, but to me it was an electric switch. I was aware of a connection.

With this new and unwelcome knowledge, I watched the other kids to assess their reactions. But they were younger than I was. So there was nothing much to watch. They continued to gabble on among themselves, giggling, pushing, yelling at one another. Even when my father would shout, "Shut up, damn you!" they'd all just disperse, regroup, and continue on as before. Well, not quite all. I focussed on Amery, aged seven, eyes wide and bright, chewing on his nails. Awake too, I thought, and felt a kinship with him.

My father didn't work as a fisherman in our little village. He was employed in the fish plant, gutting fish. Slash and gut, slash and gut, eight hours a day, five days a week, fifty weeks a year. Enough to limit the vision of any Bay Street Torontonian. I heard people in our village talk about what it was like to work with him. "A real jewel of a man," said one woman to my mother. "Patient, and right considerate. Always ready to help out." I looked at Ma while the woman was talking. I was thirteen by then, and very skillful at reading faces. She's struggling, I concluded, to keep the scorn out of her face. It was a fixed mask, telling nothing—except to me. A man friend of Pa's once said to me, "I sure hope you realize how lucky you are to have a father like him. He's some kind. A real soft-spoken man." I said nothing, and adjusted my own mask. When my father had left the house that morning, he'd yelled back at my mother, "Get your confounded books off the bed before I get home tonight! I'm sick of you with your 'smart' ways!" Then he'd slammed the door so hard that a cup fell off the shelf.

My dream was a simple one. Or so it may seem to you. I wanted to be the most talented fisherman in Mackerel Cove. Talented! I can see the incredulous looks on the faces of my Toronto colleagues. Do they really think that the profession of fishing is just a matter of throwing down a line or a net, and hauling up a fish? A good fisherman knows his gear, his boats, his machinery, the best roots to use when making lobster traps. He knows how to sniff the air and observe the sky for signs of unforecasted winds and fogs. He knows his bait, his times of day, his sea bottom, the choices of where to go and how soon. A talented fisherman knows all these things and much more. And—in spite of the wrenching cold, the disappointments, the flukey comings and goings of the fish population—he loves what he is doing with his life. I know this to be true. I spent half my boyhood tagging along with any local fishermen who'd put up with me—on their Cape Island boats, their Tancooks, or just in their dories.

No one on Bay Street can describe to you the feeling of setting out through a band of sunrise on the water, trailing five seine boats, a faint wind rising. Or the serenity that fills your chest as you strike out to sea, aimed at the dead centre of the horizon, focussed on Africa. That's what I'd longed and hoped for from the time I was five years old. At sixteen, it was still my dream.

The exam results came in, just four days before my seventeenth birthday. I stood at the mailbox, holding my marks—the highest in Grade Twelve for the whole of the county. And more. The biggest university scholarship for that region, puffed out with some fat subsistence money donated by a local boy who'd made good on Wall Street. I took all of it and laid it on the kitchen table.

"I don't want it," is all I said.

My father and mother looked at the marks, read the letter, raised their eyes and looked at me. My mother had her mask on. Not my father.

"What in blazing hell do you mean—you don't want it?"

"I don't want to go to college. I want to stay here. I want to be a fisherman. The best one around. It's what I've always wanted, ever since I laid eyes on a boat."

My father stood up. He was skinny, but he looked big that day. With one abrupt gesture, he swept everything off the kitchen table onto the floor—four coffee mugs, The *Daily News*, cutlery, Ma's books, a pot with a geranium in it, a loaded ashtray.

"You want to be a fisherman!" he shouted. "Us with no gear, no wharf, no shed, no launch. Not even a decent size boat. No, young fella! You turn down that offer and you got but one route to take. Me, I'll teach you how to do it, because I'm the best gutter in the plant."

He paused for a breath. Then again—"*No*, dammit! You just pitch out your fancy dreams and grab that scholarship, because I'm sure not gonna keep with that fool book-learning that your prissy ma seems to have passed along with her mother's milk." He smashed his fist down on the empty table, and kicked his way out the back door.

Ma died when I was twenty-four, just one week before I received my M.B.A. from the University of Toronto. I'd picked up two other degrees on the way, and had sailed through university with accolades and scholarships. There I was, half an orphan, embarking on a life of prosperity and maladjustment, cut off by my past and my present from my original dream.

I skipped graduation and flew home for the funeral. I stayed three weeks. Pa was silent and shrunken-looking, although he was only fifty-five. He sat around a lot, guzzling beer, going through two packs of cigarettes a day. The only kid left at home was Amery, and he looked as though he'd like nothing better than to jump ship. Thin and fidgety, he'd startle if you so much as snapped your fingers. He was working in the plant too. Gutting.

"Thinkin' o' closin' down the plant," said Pa, one day. "No fish worth a darn. Most o' the time, anyways. Foreign vessels scoopin' 'em all up before they has a chance to spawn."

He didn't say this angrily. He said it wearily, as though he had nothing but lukewarm water flowing through his veins. And no blood transfusion in sight.

The day I left, I waited until Amery and Pa had departed for work. Then I went out and sat on the woodpile. The offshore wind was blowing strong and dry, and the gulls were coasting around in the sky, wings spread, barely twitching. The sun was well up, casting a wide path over the ruffled water. While I watched, a Cape Islander crossed the path, low in the water with a big catch of mackerel. In the distance, the horizon stretched taut and firm, broken by the leaping waves of the four reefs.

I searched in vain for Africa. Apparently it wasn't there anymore.

Activities

1. In this narrative, the author sets up visual images of both real and imaginary places. Develop a graphic organizer that compares Mackerel Cove, Nova Scotia, with Toronto (or any other large Canadian city). Use direct quotes from the story to write a paragraph that captures the visual image of Mackerel Cove. Then use your own knowledge to write a paragraph that captures the visual image of a big city.

2. The author describes his dream in great detail. It is clear that he has a precise goal in life and is aware of what it will entail to achieve his dream. Prepare a description of one of your dreams. Include the goals that must be reached in order to achieve it. Revise, rehearse, and present your "dream" to your group.

3. The characters in the story have unique traits and personalities. With a partner, generate a list of descriptive vocabulary for each of the characters. Then discuss how these characters could be portrayed in a television version of this story.

4. In a group of four, develop the ideas you have generated so far into a script for a television version of this story. Develop a schedule or time line to prepare your presentation. Rehearse and video-tape your show for presentation to the class.

Song of the Dream People

Greenland Inuit

My eyes are tired,
my worn-out eyes,
which never more will follow the narwhal
when shooting up from the deep,
in order to break the waves of the sea,
and my muscles will nevermore tremble
when I seize the harpoon,
ijaja—a—ijaja—aje.
Wish that the souls
of the great sea animals I killed
would help me to get
my heavy thoughts to a distance.
Wish that the memory
of all my great hunts
might lift me out of the weakness of old age,
ijaja—a—ijaja—aje.

Let my breath blow a song
Of all this which calls to mind
my youth.
My song breaks from my throat
with the breath of my life.

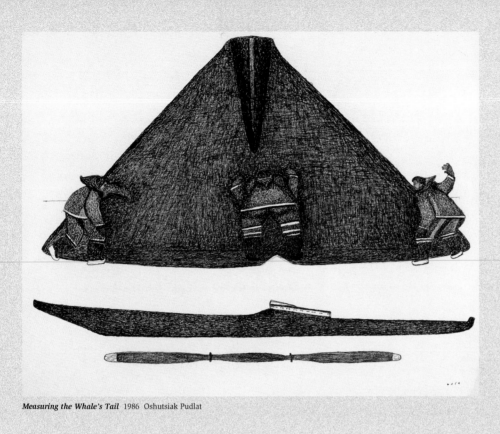

Measuring the Whale's Tail 1986 Oshutsiak Pudlat

Activities

1. The poet Stephen Spender wrote, "Great poetry is always written by somebody straining to go beyond what he can do." Discuss with a partner how this poet is trying to "go beyond what he can do." Together, consider the conflict that the poet experiences. Represent this conflict visually.

2. This song is a lament for a past time. Use the longing expressed in it to create a diamante poem:

    Title (*1 word*)
    Adjectives describing the title (*2 words*)
    Action words ending in "ing" or "ed" about the title (*3 words*)
    Nouns related to the title (*4 words*)
    Verbs ending in "ing" or "ed" about an opposite of the title (*3 words*)
    Adjectives describing the opposite of the title (*2 words*)
    Opposite of the title (*1 word*)

3. Select or compose music to accompany this poem. Be sure to choose or compose a piece of music that reflects the theme and atmosphere of the song. Prepare an oral reading of the poem accompanied by your music. Present it to the class.

Night on Gull Lake

Gwendolyn MacEwen

Sunrise Alex Colville

One island
small as a wish invited us
and the lip of our borrowed boat
scraped it like a kiss;
     our first thought was:
how many travellers before us
had claimed it, given it
a name? Or could we be
the first? Why
     did it matter so much?

Feathers and feathers fell
or so it seemed, from high
invisible gulls; our unpiratable
ship was moored to a twig;
     there was nothing to steal
from it or the island. By night
the meagre tree held a star
in its fingers; we searched
for absences, and found at last
the sinuous absence
of a snake in the grass.
It was so simple, yet
it was not. What

did we want?
We waited so long for morning
through the night of rain
which pinned us shivering against
a single rock,
and danced for joy before the dawn
when we made a miracle of fire from
some damp, protesting branches
that cracked as we stole them
        from the tree;
it was decided victory.

When we took off over
the shallow waves next day
        our pockets were full
of pebbles that we knew
we'd throw away,
and when we turned around
to see the island
one last time, it was lost
in fog and it
had never quite been found.

Activities

1. What are your first impressions after reading the poem? Write a personal reflection about the poem. Consider the following: What do you like about it? What don't you like about it? What images strike you? How does the poem make you feel?

2. The poem is written almost as if it were a journey that happened in a dream. Create a series of cartoons or visual images to represent your interpretation of this "dream."

3. Gwendolyn MacEwen uses a great deal of figurative language in this poem. Review your previous learning about figurative language, especially simile, metaphor, personification, alliteration, rhetorical question, and hyperbole. Reread the poem and find as many examples of each as you can. Write a paragraph to explain how the poet uses figurative language to develop the imagery.

FRIENDS
All of Us

PABLO NERUDA

Focus Your Learning
Reading this memoir will help you:
- formulate questions about the text
- participate in group inquiry
- focus on the theme of the text
- write a narrative story

One time, investigating in the backyard of our house in Temuco [Chile] the tiny objects and minuscule beings of my world, I came upon a hole in one of the boards of the fence. I looked through the hole and saw a landscape like that behind our house, uncared for, and wild. I moved back a few steps, because I sensed vaguely that something was about to happen. All of a sudden a hand appeared—a tiny hand of a boy about my own age. By the time I came close again, the hand was gone, and in its place there was a marvellous white sheep.

The sheep's wool was faded. Its wheels had escaped. All of this only made it more authentic. I had never seen such a wonderful sheep. I looked back through the hole but the boy had disappeared. I went into the house and brought out a treasure of my own: a pine-cone, opened, full of odour and resin, which I adored. I set it down in the same spot and went off with the sheep.

I never saw either the hand or the boy again. And I have never again seen a sheep like that either. The toy I lost finally in a fire. But even now, in 1954, almost fifty years old, whenever I pass a toy shop, I look furtively into the window, but it's no use. They don't make sheep like that any more.

I have been a lucky man. To feel the intimacy of brothers is a marvellous thing in life. To feel the love of people whom we love is a fire that feeds our life.

But to feel the affection that comes from those whom we do not know, from those unknown to us, who are watching over our sleep and solitude, over our dangers and our weaknesses—that is something still greater and more beautiful because it widens out the boundaries of our being, and unites all living things.

That exchange brought home to me for the first time a precious idea: that all of humanity is somehow together. That experience came to me again much later;

this time it stood out strikingly against a background of trouble and persecution.

It won't surprise you then that I attempted to give something resiny, earthlike, and fragrant in exchange for human brotherhood. Just as I once left the pine-cone by the fence, I have since left my words on the door of so many people who were unknown to me, people in prison, or hunted, or alone.

That is the great lesson I learned in my childhood, in the backyard of a lonely house. Maybe it was nothing but a game two boys played who didn't know each other and wanted to pass to the other some good things of life. Yet maybe this small and mysterious exchange of gifts remained inside me also, deep and indestructible, giving my poetry light.

Activities

1. Work with a partner to write questions that you have about this memoir. Then, share your questions with the class and discuss possible answers.

2. In a small group discuss this statement: If "all humanity is somehow together," as Pablo Neruda suggests, why do we continue to fight each other? Prepare a group statement summarizing your opinions, reasons, and examples. Present it to the class.

3. Pablo Neruda suggests that through the gift of a broken sheep he gained insights into all of humanity. Write your own narrative story about the most special gift you have received. Tell how it changed your life or what impact it had for you.

The Circle Game

Joni Mitchell

Yesterday a child came out to wonder
Caught a dragonfly inside a jar
Fearful when the sky was full of thunder
And tearful at the falling of a star

Then the child moved ten times round the seasons
Skated over ten clear frozen streams
Words like, "When you're older," must appease him
And promises of "Someday" make his dreams

Chorus

And the seasons they go round and round

And the painted ponies go up and down

We're captive on the carousel of time

We can't return, we can only look behind

From where we came

And go round and round and round

In the the circle game

Sixteen springs and sixteen summers gone now

Cartwheels turn to car wheels thru the town

And they tell him, Take your time, it won't be long now

Till you drag your feet to slow the circles down

Chorus

So the years spin by and now the boy is twenty

Though his dreams have lost some grandeur coming true

There'll be new dreams, maybe better dreams and plenty

Before the last revolving year is through

Chorus

Activities

1. In your journal, write down some pieces of advice about growing up that you were told as a child. Share them with the class.

2. Check in a dictionary to make sure you understand what a carousel is. If possible, get a picture of a carousel. In what way is the carousel a metaphor in this song?

3. What four ages in the life of the young person are featured in the song? Use an organizer to record the symbols used to describe each of those ages.

4. In a clear, concise sentence explain the belief about life presented in this song.

5. If possible, listen to the recording of this song. In what ways does the music capture the sense of the carousel?

1. Many of the selections in this section refer to dreams. If you could dream to be anything or anyone other than yourself, what or who would it be? Brainstorm a list of possible responses. How might your life be different? Use these ideas to write your own poem about your dreams, using any form you choose.

2. Pick your favourite short story in this section and design a children's book based on that story. Divide the story into its major parts, and draw sketches that will represent the main ideas and action. Rephrase the story in short sections that summarize the main ideas. You might choose to have the pictures tell most of the details. Work in a group to edit each others' work. Prepare the final copy and present to an elementary class or read it to a younger sibling or relative.

3. Find another poem, story, or article written by one of the authors in this section. Prepare a written critique of the piece in which you discuss the author's technique and use of figurative and descriptive language. Assess the quality of the piece, stating what you like and dislike about it. Share your chosen piece and your analysis with a partner.

4. Work in a small group to prepare a talk show in which you invite characters from three or more of the pieces to discuss their views on life. One member of the group should act as a host and the others as the invited characters. Present your talk show to the class. Be sure to remain "in character" through the presentation.

5. Use the lyrics of one of your favourite songs to create a story. Use the lyrics to form the basis of the plot, but weave your own ideas into the characters and action. Use narrative elements that you have identified in the short stories in this section. Try to use descriptive language.

6. A number of the selections in this section discuss friendship. Using these selections, and others from other sections of the anthology, work with a partner to develop a list of criteria for a good friend. Then create a poster advertising for a friend. Be sure to describe the qualities that you wish to find in a friend.

7. Many of the characters in this section are searching for their dreams. Write a letter to one of the characters, giving advice on how you think he or she should go about achieving his or her dreams.

Biographies of Contributors

Armstrong, Jeannette

Born 1948, Penticton Indian Reserve, British Columbia

Jeannette Armstrong is fluent in the Okanagan language. Her publications include the children's books *Enwhisteetkwa Walk in Water* (1982), *and Neekna and Chemai* (1984), and the novel *Slash* (1987). She has been Director of En'owkin, a multifaceted Native Education Centre. "Dust Devil" appeared in a collection of her poetry entitled *Breath Tracks* (1991).

Barnard, Denise

born 1964, Toronto, Ontario

Denise Barnard has worked as a magazine editor and writer, and college instructor. Her stories have appeared in such journals as *Intersections '93, White Wall Review 1994, Prairie Fire* and *McGill Street Magazine*. Her chapbook *Some Tings Lie So Deep* was published by Gargoyle Press in 1995. Barnard lives in Toronto.

Benítez, Fernando

born Mexico

Fernando Benítez is recognized as one of Mexico's greatest living journalists and intellectuals. He was the director of *El Nacional*, among other Mexican journals. He is the author of many books both for adults and young people.

Bradbury, Ray

Born 1920, Waukegan, Illinois

Ray Bradbury is regarded as a classic American science fiction writer. His best known works include the novels *Something Wicked This Way Comes* (1983), *The Martian Chronicles* (1958), and *Fahrenheit 451* (1967), all of which have been made into films. His stories usually mix the macabre with the humorous.

Callwood, June

Born 1924, Chatham, Ontario

Canadian writer and activist June Callwood began her career as a reporter for the *Brantford Expositor* in 1941. She has written for many Canadian newspapers and magazines, including *Maclean's* and *Chatelaine*. Callwood has also written for radio and television and has authored fifteen books. She is well known for her humanitarian efforts and has received many awards and honours, including Woman of the Year, B'nai B'rith, the Order of Canada, and the Governor General's Literary Award.

Carrier, Roch

Born 1937, Sainte-Justine-de-Dorchester, Quebec

Novelist, playwright, and short story writer Roch Carrier often uses allegory, satire, and dark humour to portray the political issues and confrontations between English and French Canadians. Much of his work has been translated into English, and he has adapted several of his novels into plays.

Conn, Jan

Born 1952, Asbestos, Quebec

Jan Conn was raised in Montreal, Quebec. She has lived in Vancouver, Toronto, Caracas (Venezuela), and Gainesville (Florida). Her first book of poetry, *Red Shoes in the Rain,* was published in 1982. She is presently an assistant professor at the University of Vermont, where she works on the evolutionary history and genetics of South American mosquitoes.

Crozier, Lorna

Born 1948, Swift Current, Saskatchewan

Poet Lorna Crozier grew up in Swift Current, and many of her poems are filled with images of the prairie landscape. She writes of human relationships, the natural world, memory, and the self. Her work includes ten collections of poetry, and in 1992 she won the Governor General's Award for *Inventing the Hawk*.

David, Lester

Born 1914, New York

Journalist and biographer Lester David has contributed nearly a thousand articles to national magazines in the United States. He has also written several biographies of prominent American political families.

De Lint, Charles

Born 1951, the Netherlands

A Canadian citizen, Charles de Lint is a novelist and short story writer as well as a professional Celtic musician. He is considered a pioneer in the field of urban fantasy, but has also written science fiction, horror, and traditional high fantasy. He is a prolific author, averaging two to three books per year, as well as writing nonfiction, magazine articles, and reviews.

Ellis, Sarah

Born 1952, Vancouver, British Columbia

Sarah Ellis attended the University of British Columbia and received her Master of Library Science in 1975. She also received an M.A. from Simmons College in Boston in 1980. In addition to her books, she also writes a column *for Hornbook* magazine, works part-time as a librarian, and occasionally teaches. Ellis won the Governor General's Award in 1991, for *Pick-Up Sticks*.

Ephron, Delia

Born 1944, Los Angeles, California

Ephron is best known for her humorous books that entertain both young readers and adults. Her first book of humour was *How to Eat Like a Child* (1978), which evolved from an article she wrote for the *New York Times Magazine*. Her many books cover everything from embarrassing teenage romance to kids and manners, all delivered in Ephron's deadpan style. Her dialogue "How to Hang Up the Telephone" is an example of her lighthearted humour.

Foon, Dennis

Born 1951, Detroit, Michigan

Playwright Dennis Foon attended the University of British Columbia, and has lived in Vancouver for many years. He has written and directed many children's plays. One of his aims is to help young people learn to cope with a complex and confusing world.

Forstrom, Dora

born 1922, Kenora, Ontario

Dora Forstrom is a watercolourist, lecturer, and art teacher. She has led delegations of North American artists to the USSR, Israel, Egypt, Greece, and Turkey. Her paintings are held in private and corporate collections in the Americas, Europe, Asia, and Australia. An illustrated collection of her short stories is currently in progress.

Foster, Robert B.

Born Victoria, B. C.

Robert B. Foster received a Masters degree in Creative Writing from Syracuse University. Later, while editing a poetry magazine in Winnipeg, he was diagnosed with several disabilities, including Attention Deficit Disorder. He currently works in Parry Sound, Ontario at an organization called RISE: Independent Living Resource Centre, where people with disabilities help each other become more independent.

Ginter, Peter

Born Germany

Peter Ginter is an award-winning photographer whose work appeared in *Material World: A Global Family Portrait.* The team of fifteen of the world's foremost photographers travelled around the world for one year, shooting 2,000 rolls of film and 112 hours of video for a variety of media. They photographed thirty families in thirty countries, living with them for a week, and at the end of the week taking portraits of the family outside its home, surrounded by all its possessions.

Hamilton, Virginia

Born 1936, Ohio

Virginia Hamilton grew up in southern Ohio. She has won many awards for her books about African-American children. Hamilton's goal is to expand the choice of subjects available for young readers by drawing on subjects from history, myth, and folklore.

Heker, Liliana

Born 1943, Buenos Aires, Argentina

Liliana Heker's first book of short stories, *Those Who Beheld the Burning Bush* (1966), together with her editorship of the "radical" literary magazine *The Platypus*, quickly established her reputation as an outspoken critic of the military dictatorship in Argentina.

Hopkins, Frances Anne

Born 1838, England; died 1918

Artist Frances Hopkins came to Canada to paint the wilderness. Accompanying her husband on canoe expeditions in Upper Canada, she painted a remarkable series of oil and watercolour paintings of the voyageurs. Her Canadian sketchbooks

became the property of the Public Archives of Canada. Most of her works were untitled, but she signed them using her initials F.A.H.

Hughes, Langston

Born 1902, Joplin, Missouri; died 1967

Langston Hughes published works in all forms of literature, but is best known for his poetry. He was a major literary figure of the Harlem renaissance, and wrote proudly and optimistically about black people. He experimented with poetic metre (rhythm) by adopting the rhythms of black music in his poetry.

Jacobs, W. W.

Born 1863, London, England; died 1943

W. W. Jacobs wrote nineteen volumes of short stories, most of which are about sailors' adventures. Ironically, his most famous work, *The Monkey's Paw,* doesn't feature sailors or the sea.

Kogawa, Joy

Born 1935, Vancouver, British Columbia

Joy Kogawa is best known for her novel *Obasan,* about the internment of Japanese Canadians during World War II. She has also written a children's version of *Obasan* entitled *Naomi's Road.* Her work addresses issues of racial and cultural diversity, persecution, and self-identity. Her poem "When I Was a Little Girl" is a personal reflection.

Kurelek, William

Born 1922, Whitford, Alberta; died 1977

William Kurelek grew up on a farm in Manitoba, and his childhood has been captured in the books he wrote and illustrated for children. A largely self-taught painter, he created a large body of work that depicted aspects of Canadian life.

LaRocque, Emma
Born 1949, Big Bay, Alberta

Educator, author, and poet Emma LaRocque received her M.A. in Canadian History at the University of Manitoba. A Métis by birth, she has a special interest in Native peoples and human rights issues and focusses much of her work in these areas. She is currently working on her Ph.D. in Aboriginal History/Literature and is the professor of Native Studies at the University of Manitoba.

MacEwen, Gwendolyn
Born 1941, Toronto, Ontario; died 1987

Though she published several collections of short stories, two novels, and a travelogue, Gwendolyn MacEwen is best known for her books of poetry. Two of these, *The Shadow-Maker* (1969) and *Afterworlds* (1987), won the Governor General's Award for Poetry.

Mar, Laureen
Born 1953, Washington

Laureen Mar's poetry has been published in several magazines.

McLarty, Doug
born 1957, Truro, Nova Scotia

As a child, Doug McLarty moved around Canada with his parents, growing up on the northern coast of British Columbia. Over a decade ago, he moved with his wife and children to the Northwest Territories, and currently makes his home in Rankin Inlet, Nunavut. He has translated the love of photography he learned from his father into a desktop design business; he also captures photographic images of the northern adventures that have inspired him to write.

McWatt, Tessa
born 1959, Guyana

Tessa McWatt emigrated with her family to Canada at the age of three. A Canadian citizen, she has worked as a book editor, ESL teacher, and translator and adapter of screenplays. Her poetry has appeared in numerous journals. Her novel *Out of My Skin*, the first in a trilogy, was published in 1998 by Riverbank Press. McWatt lives in London, England.

Mitchell, Joni
Born 1943, Fort Macleod, Alberta

Joni Mitchell's career as a singer and songwriter began in coffee houses and at folk festivals in Ontario and the United States. Several of her songs, recorded by other performers, brought her international fame. Mitchell's work has been acknowledged as a primary influence on a diverse range of "crossover" musicians. Her songs, such as "The Circle Game," have a universality that lets the listener identify with the feelings she expresses.

Mitchell, Karen L.
Born 1955, Columbus, Mississippi

While still in high school, Karen L. Mitchell won the 1973 Mississippi Arts Festival Literary Competition for poetry. She has worked for libraries, a historical society, and a literary magazine. Her book of poetry *The Eating Hill* (1989) won the Eighth Mountain Poetry Prize, adjudicated by Audre Lorde. Mitchell lives in California.

Munro, Alice
Born 1931, Wingham, Ontario

Alice Munro is an acclaimed short story writer whose collections have won three Governor General's Awards. Her stories, most of which are set in Huron County, Ontario, often address the problems of the adolescent girl coming to terms with her family and life in a small town. Her more recent work explores the lives of women in middle age, and women alone.

Nathan, Leonard

Born 1924, Los Angeles, California

Leonard Nathan is the author of nine books of poetry and has received many awards for his work. He currently teaches at the University of California at Berkeley.

Neruda, Pablo

Born 1904, Chile; died 1973

Many of Pablo Neruda's poetry collections have been translated and published around the world. Throughout his life he travelled and held diplomatic posts in many European and East Asian countries. He made his name with "Twenty Love Poems and a Song of Despair," published in 1924, and in 1971 he won the Nobel Prize for Literature.

O'Brien, Tim

Born 1946, Austin, Minnesota

Tim O'Brien began his career as a national affairs reporter for the *Washington Post* in 1973. Between 1968 and 1970 he served in the U.S. Army in Vietnam, where he received the Purple Heart. He is best known for his gripping portrayals of the Vietnam conflict.

Patten, Brian

Born 1946, Liverpool, England

Poet and children's author Brian Patten has published many collections of poetry for adults. His children's work includes plays and poems, and an award-winning mystery novel, *Mr. Moon's Last Case.*

Poe, Edgar Allan

Born 1809, Boston, Massachusetts; died 1849

Edgar Allan Poe, orphaned at the age of two, was taken into the home of a Richmond merchant, John Allan. Although Poe wrote poetry, he is best known for his terrifying and suspenseful short stories.

Prasad, Nancy

After graduating with a B.A. in English and Psychology from Queen's University, Nancy Prasad taught high-school English, and later worked part-time with the Canadian Authors Association, Writer's Development Trust, and the Book & Periodical Development Council. Poetry and fantasy are her specialties, but she also writes non-fiction, essays, interviews, and book reviews. She helped establish the haiku quarterly *Inkstone.*

Pratt, Mary West

Born 1935, Fredericton, New Brunswick

Mary Pratt graduated from Mount Allison University in 1961. She lives and works in Newfoundland. In her realistic paintings, she transforms everyday household objects—a supper table, food, a bed—into luminous works of art.

Sayyid-Ali, Mir

born Persia (Iran)

This sixteenth-century Persian painter was renowned for the strong lines, well-articulated form, and fine detail in his work. The painting "At School," which he created around the year 1540, was not done from live models. Instead, he used other artists' portrayals of students typical of that era to create this work.

Schiller, Bill

Born 1951, Windsor, Ontario

Bill Schiller has been bureau chief for the *Toronto Star* in Johannesburg, South Africa, Berlin, and London, England. He is a National Newspaper Award winner for distinction in foreign reporting and the author of *A Hand in the Water: The Many Lies of Albert Walker,* published by HarperCollins in 1998.

Seth, Vikram

Born 1952, Calcutta, India

Poet, novelist, and travel writer Vikram Seth makes use of his studies in economics and literature, in addition to travel and residency in eastern Asia and America, as background for his writings. His recent novel, *A Suitable Boy* (1993), was published to much acclaim.

Shakespeare, William

Born 1564, Stratford-upon-Avon, England; died 1616

William Shakespeare's plays are universally recognized and regularly performed all over the world. His play *Julius Caesar* has been frequently performed, filmed, and quoted. Shakespeare was also a member of the leading theatrical company of the day, which eventually made its home in the renowned Globe Theatre in London.

Thurber, James

Born 1894, Columbus, Ohio; died 1961

In his short stories, essays and cartoons, James Thurber satirized modern middleclass life. He worked at the *New Yorker* magazine for most of his life, continuing to write and publish after he became blind.

Veres, Tom

Born Budapest, Hungary

As a young boy growing up in Budapest, Veres learned his photography skills from his father. He currently lives in New York State, where he works as a photographer for an advertising company.

Wheeler, Robin

Born 1968, Calgary, Alberta

A writer since the age of twelve, Robin Wheeler has written short fiction and poetry, as well as feature stories, newspaper articles, and advertising and public relations materials. She has lived and worked in Scotland and the United States. Most recently, she acted as Editor of *Impact* Magazine and as Editorial Advisor to *Skylines* Magazine, both located in Calgary, Alberta.

Wilson, Budge

Born 1927, Halifax, Nova Scotia

Budge Wilson began writing for young adults at the age of fifty, after a career as an English and art teacher. She has also worked as a librarian, newspaper columnist, and photographer.

Wong, Tony

Born 1951, Jamaica

Tony Wong became paraplegic following an accident in 1978. He has been active ever since internationally on behalf of people with disabilities.

Credits

Literary Credits

Every reasonable effort has been made to obtain permissions for all articles and data used in this edition. If errors or omissions have occurred, they will be corrected in future editions provided written notification has been received.

p. 4 Reprinted by permission of Marcus Waddington; **p. 14** From SHORT STORIES by Langston Hughes. Copyright © 1996 by Ramona Bass and Arnold Rampersad. Reprinted by permission of Hill and Wang, a division of Farrar, Straus & Giroux, Inc.; **p. 19** From TG Magazine. Reprinted by permission of the publisher; **p. 22** Reprinted by permission of the publisher from COLLECTED WORKS OF EDGAR ALLAN POE, VOLUME III ed. Thomas Ollive Mabbott, Cambridge, Mass.: The Belknap Press of Harvard University Press, Copyright © 1978 by the President and Fellows of Harvard College; **p. 28** Appeared in *Bostonia* Magazine, No. 4, Fall 1992. Reprinted by permission of the author, Leonard Nathan; **p. 42** From HOW TO EAT LIKE A CHILD by Delia Ephron. Illustrated by Edward Koren. Copyright © 1977, 1978 by Delia Ephron; Illustrations copyright © 1978 by Edward Koren. Used by permission of Viking Penguin, a division of Penguin Putnam Inc.; **p. 44** Reprinted with the permission of House of Anansi Press, Toronto, ON; **p. 51** "Catch" From BACK OF BEYOND, copyright © by Sarah Ellis. A Groundwood Book/Douglas & McIntyre; **p. 61** Copyright © 1990 by Tim O'Brien. Reprinted by permission of Houghton Mifflin Co./Seymour Lawrence. All rights reserved.; **p. 68** From *Choices* Magazine, May 1990. Published by Scholastic Inc.; **p. 73** From SEE SAW, by Dennis Foon, © 1993 by Blizzard Publishing; **p. 85** From *Imagine Poetry Magazine*, © Prentice Hall Canada, Inc.; **p. 92** From *Resolving Conflicts*, copyright © 1996 Globe Fearon Educational Publishers, a div. of Simon and Schuster, New York; **p. 96** Reprinted with the permission of Stoddart Publishing Co. Limited; **p. 98** Recovering Anorexic; **p. 103** Used by permission of Robin Wheeler. Originally appeared in *Impact* Magazine, Jan/Feb 98, Calgary, AB; **p. 109** From *The Quiet Ear: Deafness in*

Alberto Manguel, © 1985. Reprinted by permission of Westwood Creative Artists Ltd.; **p. 213** Vehicle Press, Montreal; **p. 218** From *Gangsters, Ghosts and Dragonflies* by Brian Patten; **p. 220** From TIME magazine, August 17/98. Used by permission of Time Life Syndicated; **p. 222** From FABLES FOR OUR TIME. Copyright © 1940 James Thurber. Copyright © renewed 1968 Helen Thurber and Rosemary A. Thurber. Reprinted with arrangement with Rosemary A. Thurber and the Barbara Hogenson Agency; **p. 224** Used by permission of Charles de Lint. Originally appeared in *Spaceships and Spells*, edited by Jane Yolen. Harper & Row Publishers, 1987; **p. 234** Reprinted from *YES Mag: Canada's Science Magazine for Kids*; **p. 240** From *Reader's Digest*, June 1990; **p. 243** Used by permission of Doug McLarty; **p. 246** From the web site of The Partnership for Public Lands, Toronto: wildland@web.net. Reprinted by permission; **p. 248** Reprinted by permission of Don Congdon Associated, Inc. Copyright © 1950 by the Curtis Publishing Co., renewed 1977 by Ray Bradbury; **p. 265** Reprinted with the permission of Stoddart Publishing Co. Limited, Don Mills, Ontario; **p. 272** From *Songs of the Dream People: Chants and Images from the Indians and Eskimos of North America*. Edited and Illustrated by James Houston. Atheneum, New York, © 1972 by James Houston. Reprinted by permission of James Houston; **p. 274** Used by permission of the author's family; **p. 276** Reprinted by permission of Robert Bly; **p. 278** *The Circle Game,* by Joni Mitchell. © 1966 (Renewed) Crazy Crow Music (BMI). All Rights Reserved. Used by permission, WARNER BROS. PUBLICATIONS.

Visual Credits

pp. 4, 10 Digital composition by Tony May/Tony Stone Images; **p. 6** Reprinted with permission from Electa Editrice; **p. 12** OPTICAL ILLUSIONS by Larry Evans. Copyright © 1995 Larry Evans, illustrations. Used by permission of Price Stern & Sloan, Inc., a division of Penguin Putnam Inc.; **p. 19** Catherine Denvir. From *Images 8: The British Association of Illustrators.* London, UK. Originally commissioned by Women's Press/Macmillan Publishers, Inc.; **p. 22** Paul Eekhoff/Masterfile; **p. 26** David Muir/Masterfile; **p. 29** Illustration by Genevieve Coté. From *People Profiles Magazine*, MultiSource Series, Copyright © 1993 Prentice Hall Canada, Inc.; **p. 30** bag © Sony Inc.; postcard courtesy The Postcard Factory, Markham, ON; **p. 31** badge copyright © Trans Canada Trail/Sentier Transcanadien; pin © 4-H Clubs of Canada; magnet © Mike

Peters, Antioch Publishing, Yellow Springs, Ohio; **p. 32** Ivan Eyre; **p. 42**
Prentice Hall Canada, Inc.; **p. 51** Warren Gebert/SIS; **p. 61** "Red Sea" by
Louisa Chase. Reprinted by permission of the artist; **p. 64** Courtesy of
the Arthur M. Sackler Gallery, Smithsonian Institution, Washington,
D.C.; **p. 68** Birgitte Nielsen; **p. 70** Marko Shark; **p. 73** Prentice Hall
Canada, Inc.; **p. 88** Copyright © 1998 Mattel, Inc.; **p. 89** T-shirt copyright
© 1996; bus photograph copyright © 1997 York Region Separate School
Board, ON; stickers copyright © Hallmark Cards, Inc., Kansas City, MO;
p. 90 Down Under Shampoo bottle copyright © Belevedere International
Inc., Toronto, ON; Citré Shine Shampoo bottle copyright © 1995,
Advanced Research Laboratories, Costa Mesa, CA; recipe copyright ©
1985 World Almanac Publications, a Scripps Howard Company, New
York; **p. 92** From *At Twelve: Portraits of Young Women*. Copyright © 1988
Sally Mann. Aperture Foundation, Inc., New York; **p. 96** J.E.H.
MACDONALD (Canadian 1873–1932) *Lake Simcoe Garden* 1920 oil on
cardboard. Art Gallery of Hamilton. Presented in memory of Suzanne
Bowman 1939–1958, by her Parents and Friends, 1962; **p. 98** Copyright
© ARS, N.Y., Munch Museum, Oslo, Norway; **pp. 103, 105, 106** CP
Picture Archive (Kevork Djansezian/Kathy Willens); **p. 109** Ian
Shaw/Tony Stone Images; **p. 111** "Transformations II" by Jack Shadbolt.
Private Collection. Reprinted by permission of Doris Shadbolt; **p. 123**
From *The Owl-Scatterer* by Howard Norman. Illustrations copyright
© 1986 Michael McCurdy. Reprinted by permission of Little Brown &
Co., Ltd.; **p. 126** "Caribbean" by Jill Walker. Reprinted in *Barbados:
Portrait of an Island* by Dick Scoones, copyright © 1990. MacMillan
Education Ltd., UK; **p. 128** Button Blanket, provided courtesy of the
Royal British Columbia Museum, Victoria, B.C., 13865.; **p. 129** Sophie
Grillet/SIS; **p. 131** José Ortega/SIS; **p. 136** From *Who Hides in the Park?*,
copyright © 1986 Warabe Aska. Tundra Books, Montreal; **p. 138** "The
Zaks Family" by Peter Ginter. From *Material World: A Global Family
Portrait*. Copyright © 1994 Sierra Club Books, San Francisco, CA.
Reprinted by permission; **p. 140** Illustration by Paul Morin, copyright ©
1992. From *The Dragon's Pearl* by Julie Lawson. Oxford University Press
Canada. Reprinted by permission; **p. 141** CP Picture Archive (Dean
Bicknell); **p. 146** Frank Gallo/SIS; **pp. 152, 154, 156** Copyright © Tom
Veres, courtesy of USHMM Photo Archives; **p. 157** Permission to
reproduce courtesy of the Cincinnati Art Museum, Ohio; **p. 158** National
Museum of American Art, Washington, DC/Art Resource, NY; **p. 161**

Illustration by Cathie Felstead. From *South and North, East and West: the Oxfam Anthology of Children's Stories,* copyright © 1992 by OXFAM Activities. Candlewick Press, Cambridge, MA; **p. 163** CP Picture Archive (Kevin Frayer); **p. 166** Photograph © Ping Amranand. Printed in *Insight Guides: Bahamas*, designed by Hans Hoefer. Copyright © 1986 APA Prod (HK) Ltd.; **p. 168** pins copyright Canadian Legion; stamps copyright © 1978 Canada Post; **p. 169** poster copyright © 1997 Miramax; magnet copyright © 1994 Ephemera, Inc.; **p. 170** Illustration by John Martin. Copyright © Stratford Festival, Stratford, ON; **p. 173** "Globe Theatre Model" by John Cranford Adams, copyright © 1954. Courtesy of the Trustees of Hofstra University, Long Island, NY; **p. 174** PAOLA PIGLIA; **p. 176** © Andrew Judd/Masterfile; **p. 179** Cartoon by Aislin (Terry Mosher). Courtesy Aislin–The Montreal Gazette; **p. 183** Autumn Cycling © Rob Gonsalves 1995; **pp. 184–185** Courtesy National Archives of Canada, C-002771; **p. 186** © 1994 *Josepha: A Prairie Boy's Story*. Used by permission of Red Deer Press; **p. 188** CP Picture Archive: The Toronto Star/National Archives of Canada/PA-30212/Jessop; **p. 194** National Gallery of Canada, Ottawa; Transfer from the House of Commons of the Parliament of Canada, 1990; Courtesy of the Estate of William Kurelek and The Isaacs Gallery, Toronto; **p. 196** Copyright © 1976 Dora Forstrom. From the collection of the artist; **p. 198** Copyright © 1946 Dora Forstrom. From the collection of the artist; **p. 200** Jane Ash Poitras, Indian Art Centre Collection; **p. 203** "In the Labrador Sea" by David Blackwood. Copyright © David Blackwood. Reprinted by permission of the artist; **p. 205** Photo courtesy Joy Kogawa. Appeared in *Women: Changing Canada* by Jan Coomber. Oxford University Press Canada; **p. 206** Jim Dandy/SIS; **p. 213** Illustration © Michael J. Deas. Reprinted by permission of the artist; **p. 220** Jack Steiner Designs, photo courtesy CP Picture Archive (Marta Lavandier); **p. 221** Jack Steiner Designs, photo courtesy CP Picture Archive (Terry Renna); **p. 219** From *Saturday Night* Magazine, Dec 87; **p. 222** Barry Scharf/SIS; **p. 224** Ewen, Paterson, Canadian, 1925– , "Decadent Crescent Moon" 1990, acrylic, galvanized steel on galvanized and gouged plywood, 236 × 244.0 cm. Photo courtesy Art Gallery of Ontario. Reprinted by permission of the artist; **p. 232** mousepad copyright © 1998, Successories, Inc., Aurora, IL; card from the game *Magic: The Gathering*, copyright © 1995 Wizards of the Coast, Inc.; **p. 233** poster copyright © 1997 World Wildlife Fund; graph courtesy *The Globe and Mail*, November 16, 1998; **p. 234**